Ray has been a published writer al_____
marks the culmination of his latest _____ passion — to learn
and document as much as possible about the extraordinary life of
the West African slave Ayuba Suleiman Diallo. It was a challenge
because Ray wanted to imagine how Ayuba himself might describe
his exploits.

As a journalist and author, he has been fortunate enough to
spend almost sixty years writing about subjects that fascinated
him. At an early age, working on a West Country newspaper, he
specialised in writing about shipping and aviation. These interests
not only led to Ray taking up sailing and flying as a hobby, they also
led to an appointment as a specialist writer on the *Financial Times*.

It was not long before before Ray was given the challenge of
covering another high-profile sector: the energy industry at a time
when the North Sea oil industry was beginning to flourish. He was
not only appointed Energy Editor but awarded a Fellowship at
Harvard University's Center for International Affairs.

After spending thirteen years as a senior writer on the *FT*, Ray
joined the energy industry in executive positions. But he kept on
writing, with seven books being published on subjects that continued
to consume his interests: energy and maritime safety.

During his time within industry Ray had the responsibility
of helping to shape corporate responsibility policies within the
organisations where he worked. This led to the flowering of another
passion – environmental responsibility, and the need to reduce and,
if possible, eliminate our impact on the natural world. For over twenty-five years Ray has been a Trustee of the Young People's Trust for
the Environment. It is a passion shared with his wife, Christine, who
is a volunteer educationalist with the Sussex Wildlife Trust.

So, what led to Ray becoming consumed with interest in Ayuba's
life? A chance stroll around the National Portrait Gallery in London,
not far from his oil company office. Mesmerised by the portrait of
Ayuba, Ray was determined to find out more about the story behind
the painted gaze of this most uncommon slave. This book is the
result.

To Terry e Gina

AN
UNCOMMON
SLAVE

Happy Memories!

Enjoy

The story of Ayuba Suleiman Diallo
as told in an imagined autobiography
by

RAY DAFTER

First published in Great Britain in 2020 by
The Book Guild
9 Priory Business Park
Wistow Road, Kibworth
Leics LE8 0RX

www.bookguild.co.uk

ISBN 978 1913208 219

10 9 8 7 6 5 4 3 2 1

A CIP catalogue record for this book is available from the British Library.

Cover photograph: *Portrait of Ayuba Suleiman Diallo*, 1733 (oil on canvas), Hoare,
William, of Bath (1707–92) / Private Collection / Photo © Christie's Images /
Bridgeman Images

Printed on FSC accredited paper

Printed and bound in Great Britain by 4edge Limited

To Christine

With thanks for lifelong support and encouragement

And in memory of my father Maurice
who was a talented but unrecognised writer

Contents

◇◇◇

Preface
A journey of paradoxes

◇◇◇

This is the life story of Ayuba Suleiman Diallo, often referred to as Job ben Solomon. As a West African, born early in the eighteenth century, he shared the fate of so many of his countrymen who were captured and sold into slavery. He endured the pain and brutality meted out by thuggish sailors on board a crowded slave ship as it crossed the Atlantic. And once on a Maryland tobacco plantation, he was forced to undertake the most arduous tasks for which he was totally unsuited.

What follows in his remarkable life stretches belief and challenges our perceptions of the moral codes that persisted at that time.

So rather than provide a conventional narrative of Ayuba's life and times, written from a twenty-first-century standpoint, I have set down an account as an imagined autobiography; how he might have written it (perhaps with a good deal of linguistic assistance) centuries ago.

That has been a challenge, for this intimate story is full of paradoxes. It touches on all aspects of human emotion: from religious virtue and common kindness to the basest cruelty, avarice and exploitation. It is populated by millions of slaves. And yet for me the most troubling paradox is how, in this so-called enlightened age, we can turn a blind eye and tolerate such an abundance of modern slavery throughout the world. Maybe Ayuba's account provide some clues, if not definitive answers.

This was no ordinary slave. He was an educated Muslim of noble birth, America's first known Hafiz (an Islamic scholar who has memorised the whole of the Koran), which helped to identify him as someone special. Ayuba had himself traded and kept slaves, prior to his capture. In Maryland, he found the hardship of enslavement unbearable. He was a learned man of 'soft hands'. After falling ill and fleeing for freedom, he was recaptured. His special qualities were recognised by a group of influential men and in extraordinary circumstances he was shipped across the Atlantic to England.

Here in London, he was freed to be feted by England's royalty, aristocrats and intellectuals. He even had his portrait painted by one of the leading artists of the day. That painting, by William Hoare, today hangs in London's National Portrait Gallery; the earliest known English oil portrait of a freed slave and the first to honour an African subject in his own right as an equal member of society. That portrait was the inspiration behind the writing of this book.

Ayuba was just one of the millions of African slaves who were transported to the New World to be sold or traded in exchange for raw materials. But he was fortunate. He was probably the first black African to complete all three legs of the triangular trade route: as a shackled slave sailing one of the notorious Middle Passage routes from West Africa to a new colony in Maryland; as a nervous passenger – but still bonded as a slave – travelling in more comfort to London; and as a freeman, having been much vaunted in London, returning to his homeland in Senegambia.

Remarkably – almost unbelievably to those viewing these events through the lens of modern understanding and values – this mild mannered, intelligent man with strong religious beliefs, seemingly ignored the pain and indignity that he had endured and witnessed and returned to West Africa to assist the English in their trading activities, despite their slaving traditions. In this capacity, he found himself caught at the centre of a serious diplomatic incident: captured and imprisoned by the French, who were engaged in regional trade wars with the English. Again, he was saved from slavery and freed to continue trading.

Yet again we might fall into the trap of anachronism, reading back today's universal anti-slavery sentiments into Ayuba's life. It should not surprise us that he was not an abolitionist. Neither did he think that freedom was a universal value. Indeed, one of Ayuba's first acts on his return to his homeland was to buy a female slave to work in his own household. Ayuba had grown up in a slave-owning society. In his tradition the ownership of slaves was commonplace. They were used as agricultural workers, domestic servants, artisans, porters and guards. And it must be conceded that in general, many were treated reasonably well, often living with their owners' families. But still they were not free.

Islamic followers of the dominant Sunni sect in West Africa, including Ayuba, neither condemned nor supported slavery. And unlike a great swathe of the world's slave traders who treated their captives as mere chattels, Islam recognised that enslaved people were human beings with a right to challenge their treatment.

Sylviane Diouf explained in her book, *Servants of Allah: African Muslims Enslaved in the Americas*, that slavery was deemed acceptable by Muslims if the slave was born of slave parents or if he or she had been a 'pagan' prisoner of war. These were the rules followed by Ayuba. Boubacar Barry, a leading authority on West African history and author of *Senegambia and the Atlantic Slave Trade*, may not have referred to Ayuba specifically, but he summed up the philosophy thus, 'Slavery gave free men, especially the class of Muslim clerics, the leisure to devote themselves entirely to the study of the Koran.'

It is hard to find any contemporary description of Ayuba that is not either flattering or sympathetic. But one Protestant writer, John Green, did venture an acerbic footnote comment in Thomas Astley's acclaimed *A New General Collection of Voyages and Travels* that he edited in the mid-1740s. He was commenting on an episode in which Ayuba had praised God for the death of the tribal king of men who had captured and enslaved him. 'The folly and vanity of this man must have been very great to suppose that God should punish this King merely to revenge the injury done him, and yet let his having made Slaves of hundreds of others, go unpunished. *Job* had shewn more Humility, if not more Sense if he had imputed his own Slavery as a Punishment for dealing in Slaves himself and selling his two Brother-Negros to the Whites; though believing that they would be either eaten or murdered...'

This comment by Green might now be regarded as enlightened for that period in history. But Green omits to point out that Ayuba – an educated Muslim whose ancestors originated far to the north of the continent – would have regarded the unbelieving native black man as a different and inferior race, in much the same way as white slave traders viewed their human commodities. Indeed, it was a matter of pride that Ayuba proclaimed that members of his Fula tribe would never enslave their own.

As a man of privilege – a cleric and free man – Ayuba would have found slavery and its manual work utterly degrading and humiliating. It is unlikely that he could comprehend that such despair and misery could be felt by the enslaved from other backgrounds.

He was fortunate. His own enslavement was relatively short-lived. As such, he might be regarded as a man in a million. But this measurement of uniqueness grossly underestimates the torture, misery and inhumanity of this huge business enterprise.

It is estimated that between the late fifteenth and late nineteenth centuries, there were some thirteen million victims of the Middle Passage slave trade. A high proportion never even survived the perilous passage, for up to two million slaves died along the way; many of them were tossed into the sea to be eaten by sharks. Looking at Senegambia alone, it is estimated that up to 500,000 slaves were exported between 1711 and 1810. But even this is not the whole picture. During the eighteenth century, the population of Senegambia, including Bondu, also suffered the ravages of the trans-Saharan slave trade with Moorish raiding parties, backed by Morocco, accounting for perhaps as many as the Atlantic trade.

No fewer than 10,000 ships left Britain for the triangle trade between 1642 and 1812. More than a third of these vessels sailed from London. It is perhaps fitting, therefore, that there is a gallery in the Museum of London Docklands – just a short distance from where Ayuba landed and was given lodgings – that provides a powerful insight into the scope and suffering of the slave trade. It is illuminating, and encouraging, to read comments left by young visitors to the exhibition; 'heartbreaking', 'very sad' and 'so wrong', were three that caught my eye.

Ayuba would not live to see the establishment of the great anti-slavery movements, although he met with a number who were not comfortable with the principle of enslavement. By 1730, when Ayuba was captured and shipped to America, the Royal African Company – the official trading entity sponsored and encouraged by the British Crown – was ending its own slaving activities in West Africa to concentrate on the trading of ivory, gold and other valuable goods. But there were plenty of other independent merchants, including many Africans, who were content to continue trading slaves, often using the Royal African Company's trading posts, known as factories, as well as shipping facilities.

While Ayuba may not have been rescued by the anti-slave movement, he was influential. It can be claimed that having impressed society with his education and erudition, at a time when there were few literate black people living in Britain, he did much to show that black Africans were fellow human beings worthy of respect. This was the moral imperative that was emphasised by abolitionists later in the century.

It is heartening to see how down through the generations, Ayuba's story has become adopted to illustrate not only the noble characteristics of black people but also their intellect and intelligence. In 1831, the black editor of the *Liberia Herald*, a West African newspaper circulating in a colony of free black people, set out to refute the opinion that the 'negroes are inferior in point of intellect to the white race'. The article cited Job Ben Solomon as one of many celebrated black men who had distinguished themselves 'notwithstanding every disadvantage'. *The Gentleman's Magazine*, in 1750, described Job Ben Solomon as a 'person of great distinction'. Today, historians like Paul Gilroy are showing that Ayuba and others like him – Africans with African voices – have been central to the story of the modern Black Atlantic world.

Sadly, prejudice and racial injustice remain rife in this world. But slowly, progress in enlightenment is being made. Perhaps the most striking evidence could be found in 2018 within that most conservative of British institutions, the monarchy. Diversity and multiculturalism shone through the happy and widely celebrated wedding of Prince Harry and Meghan Markle, now the Duke and Duchess of Sussex, in terms of the great mix of invited guests and those chosen to participate. It should not be overlooked that the Duchess herself is proud of being of mixed race.

We witnessed The Kingdom Choir, a black Christian gospel group from South East London, perform a most sensitive rendition of 'Stand by Me'; a teenage cellist, Sheku Kanneh-Mason from Nottingham (the first black person to win the BBC Young Musician of the Year award), playing two uplifting classical works; and the inspirational The Most Reverend Michael Curry, the first African-American to be presiding bishop of The Episcopal Church, give a rousing address on the power of love. He clearly struck a chord with many in the congregation when he referenced the power of faith and love of those Africans who had been enslaved in America.

Given that this autobiographical account of Ayuba's life must be viewed in the light of attitudes and standards of his time, I cite as an example of the misplaced justification for slavery the writings of Malachy Postlethwayt, a British merchant and lobbyist for the Royal African Company. Recognising some people of influence had been denouncing the 'slave trade' as early as the 1740s – barely a decade after Ayuba's publicised enslavement – Postlethwayt stated his defence of the benign-sounding 'Africa Trade' in a 1745 pamphlet entitled, *The African Trade: The Great Pillar and Support of the British Plantation Trade in America*.

Postlethwayt wrote, 'Many are prepossessed against this

trade, thinking it is barbarous, inhuman and unlawful traffic for a Christian country to trade in Blacks.' But, he argued, 'the Negroe-Princes in Africa, 'tis well known, are in perpetual war with each other and since before they had this method of disposing of their prisoners of war to Christian merchants, they were wont not only to be applied to inhuman sacrifices, but to extreme torture and barbarity, their transportation must certainly be a melioration of their condition.' In short, Africans would be better off living in a civilised Christian country than among 'savages'.

I am aware how such a preposterous assertion will prompt incredulity and anger among readers; just as I am certain there will be many who will criticise the non-judgmental way in which I have set down this account of Ayuba's life. I can only state in my defence that what I have set down in this autobiography is what I have imagined Ayuba might have felt and experienced in the spirit of his time.

Let us be mindful that this despicable trade in human misery continues to flourish, albeit in a modified form. More than forty million men, women and children are still trapped in some form of modern slavery. They are forced to be prostitutes or domestic servants or are kept in bondage to work in factories or on farms, according to the Walk Free Foundation.

The UK is not immune from this scandal. The National Crime Agency reported in 2019 that in the previous year a record 6,993 people were potential victims of modern slavery and trafficking, including nearly 3,000 children, many of whom were used as drug runners. And these were only the cases referred to UK authorities. The report stated that modern slavery was affecting every city in the UK, with British nationals accounting for the highest number of cases for the first time, followed by people from Albania and Vietnam.

I have described this slave-related narrative of Ayuba's

life as an 'imagined' autobiography. However, this is no wild flight of fancy. The fundamental facts, as related, are based on Ayuba's own account, amplified by information in archived records and other published writings. It is his thoughts and, to a large extent, his conversations, that have been imagined. And it is here I have wrestled with many paradoxes.

The greatest of these is obvious. How could he have experienced the horrors of enslavement and yet returned to his homeland in Senegambia to assist England's Royal African Company in its trading activities? And why is it that as a man of strong religious beliefs and principles, he felt it was right to ensure that his own tribe should be protected from slavery while willingly condoning such captivity for those less fortunate – black Africans with little or no education or religion?

'It shows the callous attitude of our own nation towards slavery that nothing is said of the coffle of slaves which Job, the son of Solomon, had sold like cattle just before he had the same measure meted out to him which, looked at impartially, was retributive justice swiftly applied,' wrote Henry Fenwick Reeve, a long-serving British colonial officer who had spent much of his career in Gambia, back in 1912.

While, in this account, I have imagined his own experience and rationale, and in doing so offered some limited explanations, I have avoided making assumptions based on my own twenty-first-century, secular considerations. Such deep analysis I leave to others more qualified than me.

I am content in recounting Ayuba's life in a straightforward way because I regard his journey through life as remarkable enough. It is for others to interpret his motivations, religious influences and tribal instincts. Perhaps the paradoxes are too strong, which may account for why there appears to be no lasting public memorial to the unique life of this notable slave (other than his much-admired portrait).

In setting down this life, I have drawn heavily on many published works that I freely acknowledge. The primary source was *Some Memoirs of the Life of Job: The Son of Solomon, the High Priest of Boonda in Africa*, a contemporary account by Thomas Bluett, a lawyer and ordained minister who befriended and influenced Ayuba following his enslavement in America.

This short but influential account, written at the specific request of Ayuba who supplied the details of his exploits, was published in 1734, since when it has been reprinted and reproduced many times. Academics have even been moved to describe Ayuba as the 'father of African-American literature' with his book as 'perhaps the earliest biography of any African-American'. These descriptions seem to ignore the fact that he was in America as a bonded slave for less than three years. I am sure Ayuba would never have regarded himself as even part-American... or English, for that matter!

Bluett's account has been amplified through extensive research and a broader discussion of the slave trade by Professor Douglas Grant in his book, published in 1968, entitled *The Fortunate Slave: An Illustration of African Slavery in the Early Eighteenth Century*. Book reviewer J.H. Plumb, writing in *The Spectator* of September 20, 1968, observed that Grant was forced into extended discussions because 'the material for his central story – Job's capture, redemption and return – is so very thin; enough for an essay, too little for a book'.

This was the dilemma confronting me. Inevitably I have searched through many other books and archives for extra nuggets of fact and further insights. I am happy to acknowledge that among the other valuable sources have been the illuminating account of *Travels into the Inland Parts of Africa*, written by Royal African Company's agent

Francis Moore; and Professor Philip Curtin's scholarly *Africa Remembered: Narratives by West Africans from the Era of the Slave Trade*, first published in 1967.

It was to the late Prof. Curtin that I turned to arbitrate on the most suitable spelling of certain place names, a bone of contention among academics. As Curtin indicated, the nomenclature of such locations in Senegambia has always been 'shifting, contradictory, and completely unstandardised'.

I had no way of knowing how Ayuba would have depicted, in written English, such locations. As a result, I have adopted Curtin's spelling for the most-used place names in this book, such as Bondu (also spelt Bondou, Boundou, Boonda and Bundu) and Wuli (alternative forms include: Woolly, Wooly Wooli, Woolli). I trust I will be forgiven for any inconsistencies when adopting the English spelling for the names of other places, as well as people, in this book.

It should also be pointed out that throughout this book I have used the old-style Julian calendar for dating purposes. Britain changed to the new-style Gregorian calendar in 1752. So, to avoid confusion, I have avoided identifying days of the week after this date.

The use of language has caused me particular soul-searching. I appreciate the word 'slave' implies a commodity rather than a human being. 'Enslaved African' would have been preferable, but in this imagined autobiography it would not have been possible to tell the story in an historically accurate way without using the word 'slave'.

I also know the word 'negro' is offensive in today's lexicon, but in the 1700s the word was in general use to describe a person of African origin. Similarly, the description 'mulatto' (derived from the Spanish for 'young mule') may not be considered acceptable today, but back then it was commonly used to describe a person of mixed white and black ancestry.

Inevitably, my researches have taken me beyond the reading of other authors' works. It has been illuminating, and humbling, to read contemporary accounts of lives endured by African slaves in the early part of the eighteenth century. Wherever possible, I have also interrogated relevant archives, most notably in the United Kingdom and in the United States. In this endeavour I have received much valuable assistance that I am happy to acknowledge, although I fully accept that any errors or shortcomings are purely mine.

I am especially grateful to Professor Edward E Curtis IV – Millennium Chair of the Liberal Arts and Professor of Religious Studies, Indiana University School of Liberal Arts at Indiana University–Purdue University, Indiana – who provided pointers and valuable advice. In researching various archives, I tested the patience of many archivists and librarians who generously shared their time and expertise. In this respect, I would especially like to thank Dr Dustin M. Frazier Wood, Spalding Gentlemen's Society's honorary librarian; Crispin Powell, archivist to the Buccleuch estates at Boughton House, Northamptonshire; and Ryan C. Cox, research archivist for the Study of the Legacy of Slavery in Maryland, Maryland State Archives.

Philip Algar, my good friend and fellow journalist/author, once again provided literary insights and advice, as did Karen Langston, another author friend. Iman Yasser Balasaria, at Masjid Al-Noor, Tunbridge Wells Islamic & Cultural Association, patiently helped me to understand and verify some of the religious aspects of the text. Chris Pettit, a talented friend and colleague, kindly prepared the maps to illustrate Ayuba's travels. I am also especially indebted to author Ben Okri for allowing me to reproduce his inciteful poem 'Diallo's Testament'.

Others I would like to mention are Aliki-Anastasia Arkomani, Reference Specialist, Asian & African Studies, at the British Library, London; Dr Joanna Marschner, Senior Curator, State Apartments, Kensington Palace, London; Julie Cole, Julie Carrington and colleagues at the Royal Geographical Society, London; Heather Rowland, Head of Library and Collections, Society of Antiquaries of London; Catherine Wakeling of United Society Partners in the Gospel; Fiona Keates, Port and River Archivist, Museum of London Docklands; the Rev. Richard Bray, Rector of St. Anne's Limehouse, London; Lama Koubrously, at the Dar El-Nimer for Arts & Culture, Beirut; Glenn Campbell, senior historian at the Historic Annapolis Foundation; Betsy Bodziak, Director, Electronic Archives at Maryland State Archives; journalist and author Bruce Walls of Dover, Delaware, author of *Tales of old Dover*; and staff and volunteers at the British Museum, London; the National Archives, London; the Royal Archives, Windsor; the National Archives of Scotland; Delaware Public Archives; Kent Island Heritage Society; and last – but far from least – my wife, Christine, for her patience, encouragement and insights.

In tracing Ayuba's life, I have been taken on a fascinating journey of discovery, inspired by a striking portrait in London's National Portrait Gallery.

'DIALLO'S TESTAMENT'
by Ben Okri

Who can read the riddle of life
In this portrait of mine?
I am one on whom providence
Has worked its magic reversals.
Behind me are silent stories
Like a storm. I have worn
History round my neck like chains.
Freedom is a difficult lesson to learn.
I have tasted the language of death
Till it became the water of life.
I have shaped a little my canvas of time.
I have crossed seas of fires
And seen with these African eyes
The one light which neither empires
Nor all the might of men obscure.
Man is the sickness, God the cure.

This poem by Nigerian-born writer Ben Okri was commissioned by the National Portrait Gallery, London.

CHAPTER 1

Growing up in Bondu – a land of legends

◇◇◇

I stumbled out of a woodland into bright summer sunshine. Before me was a bewildering urban setting – buildings, roadways, carefully tended green spaces and people: black and white; men, women and children. All on the move. And all speaking an unfamiliar language. I tried to hide away, to make myself inconspicuous as I assessed my surroundings. I was a runaway slave, having sneaked away from a Maryland tobacco plantation where I had been inflicted with the most arduous of tasks, quite unsuitable for a man of learning with soft hands. But here, in a township I came to know as Dover, on the shores of Delaware Bay, my attempts at concealment and anonymity were futile. I just looked different. A Muslim alien in a foreign land.

Suddenly, from some dark corner, two white men of rough countenance and thick muscles grabbed me, locking my arms in their powerful grip. To the obvious amusement of passers-by, I was marched to the local jail. And there, without ceremony, I was locked behind bars. I had been taken captive once more, just like in the previous year when – as a man of noble birth and learning – I was set upon and enslaved while on a slave trading mission myself in familiar countryside close to the River Gambia in West Africa.

Was there to be no end to this misery? How could I explain to my new captors that my enslavement had been a terrible mistake; that I should never have been brought to this foreign land of America? Again, and again I cried out two words so dear to me in the hope of igniting a spark of comprehension. 'Allah. Mohammed,' I said. It was my declaration of faith; my *shahadah*.

Soon, my prayers were to be answered and after an extraordinary journey, I would be returned home as a free man. Back to Bondu. But not before my senses would be assailed with unimagined wonders in yet another foreign land.

Bondu – the land of my forefathers – is a magical place; a fertile region blessed by warm sun and irrigated by the waters of the Gambia River to the south, the Senegal River to the north and the less impressive Faleme River in the east. It is a small kingdom, providing ample reward for the enterprising Fula people who inhabit this patch of land tucked away in West Africa. Much of the time is spent raising crops and tending herds of cattle and sheep. But there are even greater gains to be made from trading.

My country's central position in the upper Senegal valley, with such neighbouring regions as Futa Toro, Bambuk, Tenda, and Wuli, has always made it a popular thoroughfare for slattees, or chief merchants, and other traders eager to do business in nearby factories, established by incoming Europeans. During my lifetime these trading enterprises were dominated by the English to the south and the French to the north. It was only natural for the people of Bondu to seek a share of this trade, including gold from nearby deposits in Bambuk, the 'Gold Country'; the teeth of elephants that roamed our land; beeswax and other riches provided by the natural world, together with the buying and selling of captives, or slaves.

It was here, in Chambey,[1] that I was brought into this world by my mother, Tanomata, the first wife of my father, in the year of 1701 and given the name of Ayuba of the Diallo family. Diallo is a common family name among we Fula people. My father, Suleiman, was a Marabout, a member of an elite, hereditary class of Muslim clerics. He rose to the highest priestly office when he succeeded his father, Ibrahima, who had moved with other migrants from Futa Toro to nearby Bondu. This happened in the reign of Bubakar Sawa Lamu, who ruled in the middle to late period of the 1600s.

The King not only appointed Ibrahima high priest, he also granted him the proprietorship and governorship of an emerging Bondu community. This background is relevant because it explains my full name, Ayuba bin Suleiman, bin Ibrahima Diallo – or Ayuba, the son of Suleiman, the son of Abraham of the Diallo family. In later life, as I was shipped to America and then to England, my hosts would find it easier to call me Job ben Solomon… and even 'Simon'.

The Bondu kingdom is crisscrossed with many tributaries and streams, which swell and flow rapidly in times of heavy rain, often making movement of people and animals difficult if not impossible. But, just as quickly, these streams disappear in the dry seasons.

The hills in the southern and central parts of the kingdom are largely unproductive and covered with scrub and woodland. There is also the forbidding Simbani wilderness in the south-west, extending into Wuli. But in the fertile lower plantations, we are richly endowed with trees such as palms, ciboa, baobob and tamarind, and pasture for cattle and sheep. Our healthy soils, which nurture sweet-smelling shrubs and flowers, are among the most productive in West Africa, suitable for planting rice, maize and millet, as well as cultivating cotton and tobacco.

The palm and the mighty ciboa trees are valuable totems of our land, providing an abundance of food, liquor, oils, timber and leaves for use in shelters, roofs, matting and baskets. Our cattle are especially precious, watched over day and night to protect them from thieves and predatory wild animals. These cows provide us with milk, meat and skins. The milk forms an important part of our diet, the liquid often being drunk when it is quite sour with the cream being turned into butter for cooking. In the same way, our flocks of sheep provide fleeces and food.

Bees, which we collect with great care from the trees about us, provide plenty of honey and beeswax. When the season is right, we collect a wide variety of fruit and berries. And cereals provide the staple foods, most importantly bread. Thus, we are blessed; able to live well but frugally in our villages of solid houses built largely of mud and dung with roofs covered with a thatch of straw and leaves.

But much more can be found in this land we call the Bondu. The playful antics of monkeys and apes provide us with a constant source of wonder and entertainment, especially to the inquisitive child. Beautiful birds, some of them dazzling in their breeding plumage, and plentiful wild fowl, add grace and calmness as well as welcome food. Wild beasts – both magnificent and troublesome, including lions, hyenas, wolves and crocodiles – present a constant threat to our cattle and asses, which means we must always be on our guard when driving our herds to fresh pastures or the river for water.

The largest of the beasts are the elephants. Their long tusks provide a valuable source of tradeable ivory. The flesh of the elephant can also be very tasty. Even greater riches are to be found in rivers and streams. There is, of course, fish aplenty; the large ones we can catch in long baskets made from cane or nets and placed in fast-flowing streams, while the small ones are caught in fine nets made from cotton. But the greatest riches are to be found in the sediment and dust washed out of the hills – gold of a very high quality.

The Fula inhabitants of the Bondu are an educated, enterprising people, brought up in the beliefs and traditions of Islam. Our language is Pular, a special version of the Fula tongue.

More tawny than black, given our origins much further north in Africa, we are proud and gentle people, recognised for our skills as pastoralists. Our cattle define our wealth. We have also become trusted traders among those with whom we sell and barter: our neighbours and travellers from further afield, but most notably, the men of the Royal African Company who have established important trading posts here alongside the Gambia River.

The company, originally called the Company of Royal Adventurers Trading to Africa, was founded with royal backing in 1660 to exploit the rich gold deposits of the upper reaches of the river. It was granted a monopoly over English trade with West Africa and its exploits soon widened beyond gold to other sought-after commodities, including silver, elephants' teeth, beeswax and, conspicuously, slaves, whom we call 'captives'. Many of these slaves might have been captured in the wars and skirmishes that occur in our land. Others would have been enslaved as a punishment for some crime or perhaps they found themselves in the wrong place at the wrong time and were just stolen by unscrupulous traders.

The use of slave labour is commonplace in these parts: black natives; largely uneducated, pagan people, who are provided with food, shelter and protection in exchange for their labours on the land or in homes. It is a matter of principle and honour that we never enslave our own people of faith.[2] Thanks to a policy introduced by my grandfather, Ibrahim, according to the laws of the Koran, all persons seeking sanctuary in Bondu are protected against slavery, providing they know God and can read. This policy has contributed much to the population of Bondu, which is now very large and flourishing.

Unlike the gold, ivory and the fruits of the land, we in the Bondu do not garner captives for the sole purpose of trading. Our first thought is to employ such captives for labour in our fields, on land and in domestic chores in our homes. But when we find such labour surplus to our requirements, we would be considered a poor trader if we turned our backs on the rewards to be gained from willing buyers.

So, this sketch provides an indication of how we live, work and earn our living. But there is so much more to Bondu.

Our lives are punctuated by prayer and quiet contemplation. We have so much to thank Him for. We take rest and relaxation in the company of our families, our wives and children and other relatives, as well as our trusted friends and advisers. We are often entertained and informed by our storytellers – esteemed leaders in our communities – who carry immense knowledge of our history and traditions. These praise singers, or griots as they are often called, provide wisdom and respected advice. And they entertain, through their musical talents and their ability to recount history and legends in such a compelling way.[3]

One of these legends, which is beginning to become popular in my kingdom in these, my later years, features the exploits of Prince Samba, with whom I grew up. We were companions and pupils studying the Koran, the Arabic language, history and other important matters under my father, Suleiman, who was the Alpha — or High Priest — of Bondu. Prince Samba's father, Siratick Gueladio, the ruler and supreme military commander of Futa Toro, had entrusted his son to the tutelage of my father because of his learning and strong moral character. I like to think that we both might have inherited at least some of the great wisdom, resolution, fortitude and ingenuity of my father and teacher. What is certain is that I was blessed to be growing up in such a privileged and spiritual environment.

My introduction to life on this earth followed the traditions of my forefathers. When I was just seven days old, our family and friends were invited to my father's house where I was named. This name, Ayuba, was written on a piece of smooth board by my father in his capacity as Priest. Then my father killed a cow, part of which was consumed by those attending the ceremony and the remainder distributed among the poor of the community. I was then washed all over with blessed water and my name was again written, this time on paper, which was rolled up and tied around my neck. There it remained until the paper was worn away.

As is traditional among Fula people, my initial care for the first two years or so was entirely the responsibility of my mother and other women in the community. As far as I can remember, these formative years were blissful, full of kindness and love, with hardly a harsh word spoken. Normally in a Fula household, a child's development is left almost entirely in the hands of his mother, with the father remaining a distant figure. In the case of myself and Prince Samba, it was my father who took charge of our religious and general education. And he was a great teacher.

While we grew up using the Fula language, my father also gave us a very good understanding of Arabic – both the written and spoken word. (Little did I know this at the time, but this knowledge was to serve me in good stead when I would move far from my homeland in later life.) Knowledge of Arabic also helped Samba and me in our Islamic studies and our understanding of the Koran.

Our life together was not wholly confined to religion and academic learning. My father also appreciated the importance of play, and in the case of boys, that meant exercising our bodies and practising being men. Play-fights were common. Samba, who was several inches taller and much more muscular than me, seemed intent on demonstrating his strength and bravery.

Samba always fought to win, whether in hand-to-hand combat or in wielding wooden weapons. He hated losing, even though this seldom happened given his more aggressive nature. When I did manage to get the upper hand, he could be quite mischievous and underhanded. One minute he would play being mortally injured and then when I began to relax in victory, he would jump up again and attack once more.

'That's cheating,' I would cry. 'You are not fighting fairly.'

Samba would always laugh at my protestations. 'You will never win in battle if you think like that,' he would say. 'If you find yourself in a serious fight, you must always aim to win, using whatever tactic is required.'

As if to emphasise the point, Samba would then strike me when my guard was down. Sometimes, I struggled to fight back tears while nursing my bruises. But I was learning the hard way that one day Samba, this young prince, would become a determined and fearless warrior.

Unfortunately, our games and studies together were brought to an abrupt end with the arrival of a large caravan of mounted emissaries and storytellers from Futa Toro. They brought the sad news that Samba's father had died. Samba was still young; at an age when a boy begins maturing into manhood. If he was distraught within himself, he must have hidden his tears in a manly way, for he showed little emotion. He might also have been determined to assume a regal air, knowing that he had succeeded Siratick Gueladio as King of Futa Toro.

The emissaries brought with them many gifts – gold, fine clothing, body adornments and weapons – as a token of thanks to my father and his household for the hospitality and schooling bestowed on Samba. I was surprised and touched when Samba himself presented me with a gold-hilted sword, a gold knife and a rich quiver of arrows.

'Look after these well, my friend,' said Samba. 'I will always be thankful for your companionship. These weapons will remind you of our time together and should serve you well as you grow into manhood. I am confident that you will grow into a fine and influential man, Ayuba.'

And with these words – delivered in princely fashion – still ringing in my ears, we parted. Although we were determined not to show it, we were aching inside, for we had become close friends. We pledged we would not lose touch and meet whenever we could but, as it would happen, it would be many years before we would be reunited. I was left to continue my studies alone.

I think that my father was pleased with me when, at the age of fifteen, I had managed to recite from memory, the whole of the Koran. There are over 6,000 verses and more than 77,000 words in this great religious text. But memorising the text – which, again, would become so important for me in later life –

was not undertaken as some form of abstract challenge. It was an essential part of my studies to become a priest and follow in my father's footsteps. For around this time – when I was fifteen – I was assisting my father as an Imam.

It would be wrong to assume that my early years were spent only in learning and following the rituals and ceremonies of the Islamic faith. Plenty of time was given to play and recreation. However, unlike girls, who played with dolls, danced and practised maternal duties, the boys' activities were focused on preparing for men's work in later life.

As I gained years and passed the important ceremony of circumcision, I was encouraged to venture further afield to tend plants and look after animals. I joined herdsmen and selected captives and helped them drive herds of cattle to fresh grazing grounds. Some of these excursions took many days, giving me plenty of time to learn from my elders the signs and warnings of the weather and the beauty and meaning of the stars in the night sky. We were often accompanied by storytellers who entertained us with stories and legends, with songs and occasionally with music played on their xylophones or stringed instruments made from calabash gourds.

Not that we ever truly relaxed, for in protecting our valuable livestock we were always prepared for attacks from wild animals, like lions, tigers and – even more dangerous – humans. We were also well-armed with ample manpower to withstand attacks from Mandingo raiding parties. They were our real enemy, at war with the people of Bondu.

The Mandingoes are tall of stature, black and a constant irritant to those of us in Bondu. Their lands are close by, lying on both sides of the River Gambia. They must be distantly related, as they come from the same heritage as the Fula people, often sharing a common language and the same Islamic faith. The Mandingoes have a reputation for being industrious, mild and social people, although in our many exchanges we find them to be warrior-like.

Their raiding parties are well-numbered and invariably well-armed, with guns, assegai, lances, and bows and arrows. But in my time as a boy, growing up to be a young man, I felt that we were more than a match. Indeed, not only did we rebuff their raids, protecting our cattle, but on several occasions, we succeeded in taking captives to add to our complement of slaves.

Trading is an essential activity within our community and here again as a boy I learnt valuable skills at the feet of my father and other elders within our community. We traded — bought, sold and bartered — goods among ourselves and with communities further afield, as well as with the representatives of the Royal African Company from overseas. Whereas the indigenous trade largely concentrated on the daily essentials of life, such as food and clothing, the Royal African organisation provided us with more sophisticated goods, like muskets, copper pans, fine textiles and beads for adornment.

Another welcome item has been the iron bar, about nine inches long. These bars are valuable commodities, not only traded but used as a form of currency, known as a trade bar, so that the value of goods can be measured against the value of a bar. Therefore, we are able to calculate how many guns, copper pans or beads we can gain by trading elephants' teeth, gold, beeswax or captives. The English have always been keen to buy these captives for whom they might pay the equivalent of seventy or eighty bars per head. An ounce of silver might be valued as one bar and for that same bar value you could also buy or trade two pounds of gunpowder or 100 gunflints.

I always enjoyed these trading activities as it meant I was able to travel far and wide — often over several weeks — and meet many interesting people from different backgrounds, some from across the seas. Sometimes my father took me and his most trusted helpers and advisers to English or French trading posts on the banks of the Gambia river, places like Gillyfree, with its small mosque; and Albreda, with a great fig tree on the northern shore of the Gambia, opposite James Island in the middle of the river, where the English have a great fort.

Further up inland, on the northern bank, lie two more important trading centres: Cower and nearby Joar. Continue travelling upriver and – about 135 miles from the mouth – and you find Yanimarew, surely one of the most attractive and welcoming ports in the whole river, with its pleasant houses and the shade of palm and ciboa trees. Much nearer to my home, in the upper reaches of the navigable Gambia, lie other factories at Brucoe and Cuttejarr with Yamyamacunda on the south bank.

There were other enticing markets and trading posts on the southern banks of the river – in kingdoms like Caen, Jagra and Jarra – but this area was controlled by the Mandingoes, and father always warned me against venturing there. These were warnings that, later in life in my adulthood, I would come to ignore at an immense cost.

As I grew older and more confident, I was allowed to venture out on my own trading missions, gaining a reputation for astute dealmaking. I was somewhat embarrassed, but secretly pleased, when my father declared at a gathering of elders, storytellers and advisors, that one day I would become recognised in many kingdoms for my skills in trading wisely and fairly.

'The kingdom of Bondu, and all the people of Futa Tora, will have every reason to be proud of their son, Ayuba,' he declared. And I blushed.

My teenage years were not all about scholarship, Islamic studies, farming and trading, however. I was also building a family of my own, taking the first of my wives to bear sons and daughters for the future. I was just fifteen when my father arranged for me to marry Aisha,[4] the daughter of an Alpha – head man and High Priest– from Bambuk,[5] just across the Faleme River from my home. Aisha was just eleven years old at the time; a slight but pretty girl.

The rituals of that marriage are still fresh in my memory. It was a traditional affair. My father had amicably agreed with Aisha's father the price of the dowry that was to be given by my father to the bride. The marriage was blessed by a priest and I was left with the challenge of coaxing Aisha from her home against the light-hearted restraint of her relations and friends. Only by showering this gathering with gifts was I allowed to lead my prize, my wife, from her home and we then made off on horseback for Bondu.

As with tradition, my wife demonstrated her shyness and bashfulness by refusing to venture out of our home without a veil for three years following the marriage. Happily, it was just two years after we were wed that I was presented with our first son, Abdullah. Later we were blessed with two more sons: Ibrahim, honouring the name of my grandfather; and Samba, named after my friend, the King of Futa Toro.

It would be another twelve years on – in about 1729 when I was some twenty-seven years old – before I took a second wife, Sadika,[4] who was the daughter of the Alpha of Damga[6] in the south-eastern part of the Tukulor kingdom which also bordered Bondu. Now my domestic arrangements changed, for – by tradition and to prevent any arguments between my wives – I shared my time and bed equally between the two. It was an amicable arrangement that helped to avoid serious friction although, as with the way with women, arguments did flare up from time to time. But it was not many moons before my second wife presented me with a bright, beautiful daughter – Fatimah, named after the daughter of the Prophet.

These were happy times. Thanks to the guidance of my father, some judicious trading activities, and success with my farming and animal husbandry, I was accumulating wealth of my own. Within another two years, I had my own plantation, three houses, eighteen servants and seventy-three head of black cattle, as well as an array of household and farming possessions. Life was good.

But all this was about to change in dramatic fashion. And the episode that was to unfold in all its horrendous, life-changing detail, has been seared on my memory to this day.

CHAPTER 2

Capture and shipment to America

◇◇◇

It all began on one of the typically pleasant days in February
1730 – dry and relatively mild for this part of Africa. The task
seemed so simple. My father, receiving news that a ship in the
service of the Royal African Company had been sighted in the
Gambia River, asked that I should immediately set off on a
trading mission. He wanted me to sell two captives into the
slave trade and buy some necessities. In particular, he wanted
paper, much sought-after for the making of the Islamic
grisgris, verses of the Koran contained in leather cases and
used as talismans to ward off evil spirits.

It was the sort of mission that I had fulfilled many times
but even so, my father issued his usual warning: 'Remember,
son, do not venture across the river into the lands of our
enemies, the Mandingoes,[7] for they offer nothing but trouble.'
My father paused, and then with a stern face, he spoke again
with emphasis: 'Beware at all times.'

Despite the dire warnings, I departed with a light heart, accompanied by two servants and two captives who were to be sold. We set off on foot for the important slave market at Joar, a journey of some 200 miles to the south-east of Bondu. Joar is situated in the kingdom of Barsally, conveniently placed near the middle reaches of the River Gambia, on the northern shore, about one hundred miles upstream from the mouth of the river. The small community is a popular trading post, situated at the convergence of several trade routes.

The River Gambia at this point, a little upstream from the horse-shoe bend with its greatly wooded Elephant Island, provides a safe anchorage for trading ships and, approaching Joar, we received confirmation that such a vessel, the slave ship *Arabella*, had recently arrived from London. Confident that I would quickly fulfill this trading mission, I changed my plan and decided to go immediately to nearby Cower, the main trading post of the region. Cower is a great trading centre, renowned for its imported cotton fabric, so popular with the women of this region who love fine, brightly coloured clothes. But on this occasion, it was the slave market that attracted me. There I found Captain Stephen Pike, Master of the *Arabella*, bidding for slaves.

This sour-faced officer took a cursory glance at my two captives and offered an insultingly low price that I knew my father would never have sanctioned. So, rather than make the deal and face chastisement on my return, I decided to venture elsewhere to sell the captives. And, despite my father's warning, I chose to cross the river to trade with some Mandingo acquaintances, as I had done on several occasions in the past.

On this occasion, I thought it best to send back to my father the two servants to explain my intention. At the same time, I engaged the services of Lamine Ndiaye[8] who was also a Fula from Bondu. He was well known to me; a trusted guide and interpreter who understood the language of the Mandingoes. I knew he would be a great help if I needed to bargain with these people.

We took a canoe across the Gambia and then started walking downstream on the other side towards Tancrowall, a large town in the kingdom of Caen, some sixty miles distant, where I knew there was a newly settled trading centre. This was also the place where Antonio Voss, a very successful Portuguese merchant, lived and traded. I knew he was well known to the Royal African Company and English traders on the River Gambia.

I felt confident that if I could not find a ready buyer for our captives during our journey through the countryside, we would certainly be able to trade in Tancrowall. In the event we were fortunate, for along the road we were not only able to sell the two captives for an attractive price but were also able to acquire twenty-eight head of cattle. I felt very pleased with myself for concluding such favourable transactions.

'It is time to return home, for we have done well,' I said to my companion. I was confident that my father would see that the acquisition of valuable cattle would more than compensate for my failure to purchase paper.

Our intention now was to drive the cattle back upstream and cross the Gambia by raft at Yamina, on the opposite side of the river to Cower. As we were drawing close to this crossing, near a community called Damasensa in the kingdom of Jarra, I decided that we should visit a friend and refresh ourselves at a nearby Fula village where I knew we would be made welcome.

Demonstrating typical Fula hospitality, my village hosts offered Lamine and I refreshment as well as shelter from the midday sun. Feeling tired and relaxed, it was not many minutes before we were both in deep slumber.

That was a big mistake. We would now suffer a great penalty for being so much off our guard; for journeying without being sufficiently watchful.

We had been quite oblivious to a band of villainous Mandingoes – there must have been seven or eight of them – who had silently followed us to our resting place, tempted by the prize of our possessions. In my tiredness, I had carelessly taken off my sword, knife and quiver of arrows – all treasured gifts from my friend Samba – and foolishly hung them up inside the hut.

Without us striking a single defensive blow, the Mandingo bandits grabbed these treasured weapons, shouting words that I could only assume to be abuse and insults. I was resigned to the fact that they would make off with this valuable prize, as well as all our newly acquired cattle. We had no chance of resisting given their strength of numbers, ferocity and the fact that our few hosts had quickly disappeared in fear.

Then we were confronted by an even greater horror. It became obvious that our enemy was also intent on taking us captive as well. As we were roughly manhandled and tethered, I frantically cried to Lamine, 'Tell them who we are. Tell them I am a man of faith, the son of a priest. I have friends here!'

Whatever was said, it had little effect. If anything, we were handled even more brutally. We were stripped of our robes and made to stand in only our undergarments.

'This is madness,' I cried. 'We are not savages. You cannot do this to us.'

The Mandingoes remained resolute. We were subjected to even greater ignominy. For, with our hands and feet bound and our bodies being held prone by the biggest – and the most foul-smelling – of our captors, our heads were shaven, and our beards were cut to a mere stubble.

Now I was really angry.

'I will not stand for this gross indignity,' I shouted. 'This is sacrilege – an insult against none other than Allah!'

Heated words were exchanged between my interpreter and our captors. And then Lamine explained, 'Master, they say they have no wish to insult us or our faith. They just want to make us appear like prisoners, taken in battle.'

I could see clearly our horrible fate. I knew full well that it is customary to shave the heads and beards of pagan natives who then become marketable captives.

We were going to be sold as slaves!

'Allah be merciful,' I cried.

Still tethered and roughly manhandled, we were marched the short distance to the river where we made the crossing to Cower and the slave market we had visited only a few days earlier. Although I was still smarting from the indignity of having been transformed from master to slave, I was now beginning to think more rationally. Surely, we would be given an opportunity to explain our position and to negotiate our freedom. The Fula are charitable people. We never sell each other into slavery, and we see it as our duty to redeem any who are taken and sold. I became increasingly hopeful that we would be freed, or at least ransomed in exchange for our freedom, if only we could make the slave traders understand.

My immediate optimism was quickly shattered when I realised that our captors were selling us to none other than Capt. Pike of my previous encounter, an experienced independent slave trader, who I later learnt was in the service of Capt. Henry Hunt, a brother of a well-established merchant based in Little Tower Street, London. The fateful trade took place on Friday, February 27, 1730. It is a date stamped on my memory; as permanent as any slave branding that I feared but, for some reason, I managed to avoid.

If Capt. Pike recognised me, he barely showed it, for

quickly my companion and I were forced into line with some twenty other captives – I hate to use the word 'slave' – where we were shackled together by the neck with leather thongs. Those of us who resisted or shouted our objections were brutally beaten with sticks or repeatedly whipped across our backs and shoulders. Few of us were left without angry red weals across our bodies.

The pain of our injuries was nothing to the gross indignity we were to endure as our brutish captors forced us all – men, women and children – to strip naked for the obligatory inspection. We were gripped tightly as probing fingers examined us intimately to ascertain our state of health. Our teeth, eyes, ears, limbs and private sexual parts were scrutinised as though we were slaughtered slabs of meat. It mattered not whether we were male, female or a child.

At first, we were kept ashore, shackled together in this sorry state. There was much moaning and wailing as we lamented our fate and suffered repeated beatings in consequence. We were being sustained with the merest portions of food and water. Some even refused this meagre sustenance, preferring to starve rather than face slavery. These desolate souls kept their mouths firmly clamped shut as their captors attempted to force-feed them. In the end, hunger, thirst and torture forced them to relent, but I learnt that many slaves did succeed in their quest for oblivion during their passage to the Americas.

Then on Sunday, March 1, we were forced to shuffle in line onto the *Arabella*, a ship smaller than many in the trade but from outward appearance one that was of sound construction. In time, we were led down into the holds, but not before we were again stripped naked and examined head to toe, this time by the ship's surgeon. No doubt he was anxious to weed out those of us close to death's door so that the numbers of who would be lost during the voyage could be kept to a minimum. There is little gain to be made from selling bad fruit.

With the help of Lamine, with his linguistic skills, I managed to explain to one of the traders that we were of Fula heritage and certainly not captives. I knew that the Royal African Company factories would not buy any slaves unless they were certain they were entitled to be sold. But experience has also taught me that in this market – as in any market – rules can be bent, and blind eyes can be used for scrutiny. Then Capt. Pike appeared, providing me with an opportunity to explain that I was the same man that had come to trade two slaves with him a few days earlier.

'You must let us go,' I pleaded through an interpreter. 'This has been a big mistake.'

Capt. Pike thought for a moment before declaring, 'I have a job to do, quotas to meet, and you have been brought to me in the normal way as slaves. You are too valuable for me to just let you go.'

He paused again, perhaps for effect, and then added, 'Although you refused my offer of a trade before, I am willing to give you another opportunity.' We listened, carefully, waiting for the captain to specify the deal. 'I am willing to ransom you, to give you your freedom, for the price of two slaves apiece.'

Given that we had nothing of value in our possession, indeed no possessions at all, to undertake this trade ourselves, we were given the option of seeking money or four captives from my father. An acquaintance of my father who lived nearby at Joar was contacted and he, in turn, immediately sent a fleet-footed messenger to Bondu.

Capt. Pike had raised our hopes for a brief spell. Such was our despair Lamine and I would have clutched at any passing straw. But reality soon enveloped us in our deepest anguish. Bondu was a great distance away. It would take many days for the messenger to reach my father – even if he managed to complete the journey through the wilderness, avoiding wild beasts and Mandingo raiding parties. And then my father had to assemble captives and depute messengers to retrace the journey to bring them back to the ship.

Time progressed so slowly as we waited in increasing anxiety, tethered to our fellow slaves in the hot and stinking holds. And all the time more and more slaves were brought on board the *Arabella*.

As the days passed we became familiar with the dull routine of a human cargo. For the most part, we sat or laid in a state of utter despair. There was little conversation; merely groans of despair and cries of pain. I kept my eyes shut for much of the time, trying to recall happier times as a way of trying to relieve my aches and pains. I would often find some solace in silently reciting prayers and passages from the Koran.

Twice a day, small groups of us – about ten in number – were taken from the holds under armed guard to the main deck, where we were given food and water. The first of these meals was in mid-morning, while the second was in mid-afternoon. The food was basic in the extreme, invariably little more than a boiled pudding of ground corn flavoured with palm oil, salt and peppers. Every other day or so we were also given a portion of broad beans – or horse beans, as they were called on board – shipped out from England. Some of us, at least, came to look forward to this small variety in our diet, even if the unappetising beans were supplied more for the benefit of our digestive systems than our palates.

While we waited in the Gambia River, the only time we were able to breath fresh air and feel the sun on our backs was when we – the men – were brought to the main deck for messing or when we were allowed to use the overhanging privies, situated on each side of the ship. These privies, mounted by broad ladders, seated about twelve apiece – added even more to the indignities suffered by slaves.

In order to exercise even more control over this live cargo, male slaves were separated from the women and children. For instance, the women messed on their deck with the crew where, no doubt, they had to endure many lascivious glares and suggestions – and probably much worse – while boys and girls ate alone, a distressing experience.

At all times, discipline was strict and harsh. Any sign of disobedience or rebellion was punished with a whipping or the application of thumb screws, as well as a warning of much more severe punishment if there was such reoccurrence once we were at sea. Some around me refused to eat, declaring they would prefer to starve to death than endure the unbearable hardship that faced them. But such obstinacy was not tolerated. The slavers prised open their mouths, sometimes with gruesome metal tools, to force food and drink down the poor souls' gullets. They were also threatened with torture.

The crew was intent on instilling an atmosphere of fear and acquiescence among the captives while still in the confines of the river to lessen the chance of an uprising or mutiny while at sea. I had heard that insurrection on the part of slaves, threatening the lives of all on board, was more prevalent in ships leaving these shores than from any other African region.

Long days passed, and more and more captives were loaded, filling every available space. By now our allotted resting place had been reduced to just a few feet wide. We were arrayed like elephants' teeth, just about able to lay down, head to toe. The sweaty atmosphere below was pungent with the smell of vomit, urine and evacuated bowels, for many of we tethered slaves found it impossible to control these bodily functions.

The noise of wailing and moaning at times became unbearable. This was hell. But we were still captives in an inland floating jail. I could only imagine – and fear – what life would be like when we set sail. For by now I knew that if the ransom did not arrive very soon, we would be bound for America.

One evening – probably now late in March, although I had completely lost track of the passing days – Lamine and I were separated from our fellow sufferers and escorted to Capt. Pike. My heart pounded with rising excitement, as by now I fully expected that my father had been successful in delivering the required four captives or at least the value in iron bars. But this euphoria was short-lived.

'We are now fully loaded, and we leave first light in the morning,' said the captain. 'As there is no sign of the ransom demand being met, both of you will be kept on board and traded as legitimate slaves when we reach Annapolis in Maryland.'

I protested but was abruptly told to hold my tongue.

'You're learning a hard lesson,' said the captain. 'You should have accepted my price when you first offered me those two slaves.' I sighed. But he continued, 'The fact that you did attempt to trade slaves poses a problem, both for you and me. If your shipmates learn that you are a slave trader, I fear you would not last very long on this voyage. I cannot imagine the torture and death that surely each of you would face. On the other hand, I want a quiet ship – free from fighting and rebellion. I know how quickly anger and hostilities can turn to mutiny. The whole ship could be endangered. And I want to sail again. Often! There must be no mention ever again of your active roles in this trade.'

We were dismissed. But just as we were about to be led away, Capt. Pike smiled, almost benignly. 'In a few days' time, after negotiating our way downriver, we will be calling in to James Island[9] for our final provisions. If, by any chance, your father's messengers are there with money or the four slaves, you will both be free to leave. In many ways, I hope this transpires – but I would not raise your hopes too high.'

Slowly our ship made its way downstream, until the afternoon of April 11 when a murmur went around the ship signalling that James Island had come into view. It was hard to conceal my mixed emotions – keen anticipation along with a sense of foreboding – as I lay below in the heat and gloom of the hold, tethered to my companion and other unfortunates. Then a group of us was led into the sunlight for our usual messing and privy routine.

What we saw was truly impressive. There before our eyes on this small island was a well-constructed fort run by the Royal African Company. It appeared ideally situated, being in the middle of this great river, about two miles from either bank. The fort itself, built of stone, was square-shaped with four bastions. The building was well-defended with many cannons and guns.

Protected within the fort were apartments for the Governor, chief merchants and traders, as well as storerooms. There were separate stone-built barracks to house the lower ranks, including a 'negro house' big enough to accommodate some 200 souls, as well as further storehouses.

As we drew nearer, I could see the island was teeming with people: many black people – slaves and African servants – together with a troop of English soldiers and a good assembly of white men; senior officers of the company together with traders and writers. Another trading vessel, the *Mary*, was anchored a short distance from the fort and there was great activity as essential provisions, including more than a few barrels of liquor, were ferried ashore. Lying close to the island was a flotilla of small, shallow-bottomed boats and canoes that were used to carry people and goods to and from the shore as well as upstream into the upper reaches of the great river.

But it was not all this hubbub and activity that was really holding my interest. As our ship dropped anchor, I eagerly scanned the shore, battlements and every other vantage point in the hope of catching sight of my father or some of our servants, along with the required captives. But I was mortally disappointed. There was no sight of them. I was in a desolate state as I was led back down to the fetid hold.

This routine was repeated several times over the next day or two. Each time I would reach the deck in hope and anticipation, and each time I would return in despair. But then, on the last occasion, the ship's surgeon took me aside. Although I was mildly curious why I had been separated from my fellow captives, I was not wholly surprised. More importantly, neither were the other slaves, for it was often the case that the surgeon selected individuals for medical examinations. However, it quickly became apparent that the manner of my selection was merely a way of deflecting interest and suspicion away from others. It is so hard to keep secrets when you are all tethered in captivity.

I was led to Capt. Pike who, through my interpreter, explained that he had received no news from Bondu.

'I have been delayed long enough. I cannot wait any longer,' he said. 'We sail on the next tide. I remind you again, you must on no account draw attention to yourself. The first sign of trouble and I will act quickly and harshly. You must expect to be treated like all the other slaves on this ship. Your new life as a slave begins here.'

I was then led below to be reshackled to Lamine and the other poor souls packed in the dark, stinking hold. I lay there in silence for what seemed like an eternity and then I heard the anchors being raised. I finally accepted I was about to be transported as a slave to America. Silently, and with eyes shut tightly, I began to recite the verses of the Koran.

Within a matter of hours, we were allowed on deck to find that the *Arabella* was well on her way, entering the wide expanse of the Gambia estuary. Behind us I could see another ship – I was told it was the slave trader *Elizabeth* that had also been loaded at Joar. I needed no further confirmation that the trading of slaves from this part of Africa was indeed a major business; a trade that was undoubtedly lucrative but one that I was now learning could also be measured in terms of its hardship, misery and, for the most part, unjustness.

I was despondent and totally unaware that I had almost escaped this terrible fate. Much, much later I received word that the loyal and doughty messenger had succeeded in reaching Bondu to deliver the message. My father had then sent messengers with several slaves to secure our release from Capt. Pike, but by then our ship had sailed. I was also told that Samba, my friend the King of Futa Toro, had also sent a war party to raid and kill a great number of Mandingoes in retribution.

But this was all too late.

I was plunged into a state of even greater depression as we left the warmth and abundance of my dear Africa and entered the mighty Atlantic Ocean at the start of what the traders called the Middle Passage, that expanse of storm-tossed sea that would take us to North America. But I was not tormented by the frightening prospects of this passage. My thoughts and concerns lingered over my father, wives, children and all in Bondu whom I had failed and abandoned. I had been shown to be a fool for disobeying my wise father. I had betrayed my fine upbringing, the careful education and my religion. And lying next to me, as a constant reminder of my failures and stubborn stupidity, was poor innocent Lamine Ndiaye, who I had led into this hellish nightmare.

Through all this adversity Lamine remained a loyal friend. Remarkably, not once did he challenge me or complain about my part in his adversity.

Our voyage was hellish and yet, in retrospect, I can imagine that in the most violent of storms it could have been even worse, given our dark, cramped, hot and smelly surroundings down there in the bowels of the ship. We had no greater room to move than we had when we were easing down the River Gambia. Cries of anguish and pain were constant accompaniments to our incarceration.

And there was always movement; frightening and uncomfortable when the swells increased, tossing about our vessel with its packed human cargo. Many cried out in anguish as we lay helpless, wondering whether the ship would break apart around us. It was in these conditions, with portholes closed adding to the suffocating conditions, that many of us failed to control our stomachs – and, in some instances, bowels – all of which contributed to the stench and filth around us. When the storms died down, the healthiest among us were made to wash and scrape the decks, which were then doused in vinegar to help prevent disease.

When we were sailing in more kindly seas, we were often unshackled and allowed on deck to exercise – and even dance. While we welcomed this freedom, and this opportunity for expressing our emotions in dance, I cannot say we took part in a truly joyous manner, as we would have done back home. We were all too aware that beatings and other punishments would be inflicted on anyone who resisted and refused to take part.

On most of these occasions these periods of comparative relaxation lasted several hours, but I recall one notable time in the most benign sailing conditions when we were allowed to breath in fine, fresh air from late morning to evening. Clearly Capt. Pike had reasoned that out here in mid-ocean we were unlikely to jump ship and that contented slaves were less likely to mutiny. But we could not be fooled. We knew there was a sound business reason for being allowed such freedom and exercise. The crew were ensuring that we – the ship's cargo – were being kept in as good a condition as possible to secure the best prices on our arrival. In this endeavour it seems Capt. Pike was reasonably successful.

The crew of some twenty men were among the most uncouth, foul-mouthed and, at times, cruel seamen that you might encounter on the high seas, for only the most desperate of men accepted work on a slave ship, given the terrible heat and conditions, the risk of illness, and the ever-present threat of rebellion among the captives. That said, under orders from the master, they did manage to keep most of us free from any serious harm.

There was a distinct change of mood among *Arabella*'s cargo of captives as we made landfall at Cape Henry in the Colony of Virginia. While there was relief that we had survived the crossing from Africa our overriding emotion was one of real fear. How would we be treated – how long would we survive – in this new country? Would we ever again be free? Would we always be parted from our families and friends in Africa and would we die in this forbidding land that we saw before us?

Our anxieties seemed to be amplified by our slow progress, for Cape Henry was not to be our ultimate destination. We were made to wait for fair winds to carry us northwards up the sheltered waters of the Chesapeake. Finally, we made our way, with Capt. Pike successfully navigating past such maritime hazards as the Middle Ground and Horseshoe Shoal, until we arrived at Annapolis, a thriving shipping port and capital of the province of Maryland.

When we were led ashore in Annapolis, probably no more

than two months after our departure thanks to favourable Atlantic winds, there were still some 150 of us remaining to be traded. Less than twenty had succumbed to illness; mainly the flux or fever. Or maybe some had fallen into such deep despair that they had willed on death to avoid the hardship of slavery in America. I knew from stories told in the trading factories back in my homeland that the number of dead cast over the side during our passage was far fewer than on many of the ships in this trade.

The day of our arrival in the New World was bright. The sun may not have had the intensity as in my homeland, but it was comfortably warm, to my relief. I had heard such dreadful tales of the harsh conditions endured by captives in the bitter coldness of these parts. But if the climate was benign, the looks and countenance of the welcoming party sent a chill through me.

'I do not like the look of these people,' I whispered to Lamine. 'They stare at us in a stern manner, as if we are no more than wild animals. I would look kindlier on any cattle that I was buying. I hate to think what fate awaits us, Lamine. Stay strong my friend and…'

The conversation was brutally interrupted, because at that moment I was jabbed in the side with the blunt end of a trader's whip – a painful warning of more serious treatment if I did not keep quiet and follow the shuffling line of tethered slaves along the quay.

CHAPTER 3

A slave in Maryland

◇◇◇

Never had I experienced such a bewildering and frightening mix of emotions as those that were coursing through my body on that fateful day. The sun was shining. I was in a new land. And some of the sights were truly wondrous. Behind the riverfront wharves and warehouses, there was a great expanse of land, there on the banks of a river – the River Severn, as it became known to me – with dusty roadways and lanes already in place. Domesticated animals, cows and horses seem to be free to wander at leisure, while the settlement itself appeared as if in its infancy.

True, there were several substantial buildings constructed of brick and wood, including the church of St Anne's, with its spire and bell, that were far more substantial and ornate than anything I had witnessed before; even on James Island. And yet this sparsely populated settlement was far less ordered than the more rudimentary buildings of my African township.

Individual homes were scattered here and there, in a most irregular fashion.

I was also pleasantly surprised to see the free and easy way in which the local population ambled around the settlement, as if without a care in the world. And yet what dazzled my eyes and confused my brain most of all was the way in which black and white people seemed to move freely, with little if any discernible animosity between them. There seemed to be as many black people as those who were white although, over time, I discerned the black slaves and servants probably accounted for a quarter of the population. Some black couples – I assume they must have been servants – were even accompanied by children. This was not what I had expected. After all, we had often been told that captives never returned from this hellish place; that it was not uncommon for those made slaves to be beaten, killed and even eaten by the slave owners in this New World.

Maybe these sights were being distorted by misted eyes, for I could not escape the fact that my current predicament appeared bleak and utterly humiliating. As a new arrival, the overwhelming impression was still one of misery and torment as we shuffled along, a snake of virtually naked humanity, to be prodded, sorted and separated. Even those I knew to be related, including a family with children, were being roughly manhandled apart and taken in different directions to be viewed, mauled and sold. I knew then that Lamine and I were almost certainly about to be parted and I felt such anguish and sorrow that I had led this loyal and educated man into this desolate situation.

'I'm so sorry,' was all I could say.

He nodded with kindness in his eyes. I promised that if ever I gained my freedom, I would do my best to ensure he too would be set free. Again, he nodded without a word, but this time with more of a resigned expression. Then we were parted. I knew that probably I would never see Lamine again; that I was alone in a foreign land, unable to make myself understood and with little prospect of pleading for my freedom. I was about to be treated in the same way as the most miserable, low-caste captive that you could encounter in the African wilderness.

After being poked, stroked and displayed like an animal about to be added to some herd, I was led by Capt. Pike and delivered to a gentleman named Vachel Denton. This Mr Denton was a leading figure in Annapolis, the owner of several plantations in Maryland and an attorney for William Hunt, the London merchant brother of Capt. Henry Hunt, Capt. Pike's employer. Although it seemed I was being treated as harshly and dispassionately as any of the other poor enslaved souls, I suppose I could take some satisfaction from being identified by such a prominent person. But I was not to remain in this distinguished company for long.

Very quickly, and still on the quayside, Mr Denton sold me on to another man who did not appear to me of such high status. It transpired that this was Alexander Tolson,[10] who owned a tobacco plantation across the water from Annapolis, on Kent Island in Queen Anne's County. I was sold, just like a cow, for the equivalent of forty-five English pounds. I was even stripped of my identity, for my new owner assigned a new name for me; one that he could easily remember. I was told, with the aid of gestures, that henceforth I was to be known as 'Simon'.

Kent Island, lying seven miles across Chesapeake Bay from Annapolis, was one of America's earliest settlements, not that the history or the beauty of its setting was of any comfort or interest to me in my new life under a new name. Our small boat took us to the ferry landing at a settlement, called Broad

Creek. This emerging township had an array of scattered houses, a courthouse, a jail, tavern and a church.

But it was its people who caught my eye and instilled a measure of unease in my soul. For those gathered on the landing stage – and they were mostly white – were staring at me, perhaps inquisitive of my unusual features. Leaving Broad Creek, Mr Tolson, riding horseback, led me as I walked inland across flat, undemanding countryside to the plantation, about two miles distant. Here my spirits were lifted somewhat by the tranquil setting: well-attended fields of tobacco bordered by woodland and irrigated by small creeks.[11]

On arrival on the plantation I was shown to my accommodation, a simple but well-constructed wooden hut shared with several other slaves, none of whom spoke Fula or Arabic. Our quarters were situated some distance from Mr Tolson's main house, so at least we were allowed limited freedom to do as we wished; that is, when we were not working or sleeping from the sheer weariness of our exertions.

In time I gradually adjusted to my new life. Work was hard, very hard, driven by Mr Tolson's men who took no account of our tiredness or day-to-day illness. That said, we were treated less harshly than I had feared, fed reasonably well – even if the food was somewhat monotonous – and provided with sleeping and washing facilities that were at least adequate.

Just like on board the ship, from time to time we captives were encouraged to relieve tensions and passions by dancing, sometimes in a ring, to the beat of drums. Here, however, there was little fear of being beaten for refusing to take part. Our strength was needed for work and Mr Tolson seemed genuinely concerned about maintaining a healthy and contented workforce.

Perhaps this was the reason why, in time, I was moved from the communal hut to a smaller building in which only two other slaves were accommodated. They proved to be quiet, affable company, even if we could not make ourselves understood in a common language. I believe that Mr Tolson recognised that I came from a different background from the predominantly black captives and as a religious man, he had seen I had my own religious needs and practices.

With the use of observation, very basic English words and plenty of sign language, I came to appreciate more of the social structure of the wider plantation community that I had found so bewildering in the early days. Given our relative freedom – at least free from shackles – it was not uncommon for slaves and servants to mix and socialise. This went for both men and women. Neither slave nor servant was allowed to marry but they could, and did, have children. Indeed, a newborn child was deemed to have added to the wealth of an owner, for the child automatically took the status of his or her mother, whether she was a slave or servant. Even the mulatto child of a free white man and a slave woman was regarded as a slave. And I came across quite a few of these children during my time on Kent Island.

I could only observe, for I had little desire – or, indeed, energy – to engage in such base activities. Quite simply, I was ailing. When I succumbed to captivity in Africa, I prided myself on my fitness for, although I had never had to endure the harshness of hard labour, I had never shirked my responsibilities. Here in Maryland, probably weakened by my voyage to the New World, unaccustomed to the change in climate and lacking sufficient nutrition from unfamiliar food, I found the severity of my labour overwhelming. I shared some of the heaviest work on the plantation.

Apart from preparing the land, planting and tending the crops, we had to harvest and cure the tobacco before stuffing the pungent-smelling leaves tightly into large barrels called hogsheads. These barrels, which were four feet in height, could weigh the equivalent of six or seven men when fully packed and each of them had to be manhandled by slaves. The barrels were either rolled on to shallow-draught boats or lifted onto wagons for transportation to waiting ships.

Against all my best endeavours, I weakened and became increasingly distressed. Soon illness was taking control. I feared the worst, but I was fortunate in that Mr Tolson seemed both a perceptive and kindly man. A Christian churchgoer, he often displayed the gentility I assumed was associated with his English upbringing.

Mr Tolson was a family man who gave every appearance of being happily married to his wife. Although not particularly robust in body, he worked diligently overseeing his business with the support of his six sons and two daughters. The family, in turn, was helped around the house, kitchen and garden by several African slaves, both male and female. These I espied only from afar, as my place was in the fields, under the command and watchful eyes of overseers. It was Mr Tolson who was the first to recognise, or at least acknowledge, that I was somewhat different from other slave workers and unused to heavy work.

By this time, I too had come to appreciate that if I had shown my captors my hands, I might even have been spared the indignity and hardship of slavery. Slave raiders and traders preferred the less-educated, roughest and most hardy species of humanity to labour in captivity. They tended to avoid the privileged 'smooth negroes', as we were called. And I had those soft hands.

And so it was that Mr Tolson relieved me of my plantation duties and put me to herding cattle. While this activity was much more to my liking – and even my experience, for I prided myself that I understood the way of cattle – I was still weighed down by illness and the indignity of enforced labour. Slavery was for much lesser mortals.

Fortunately, I was able to find solace in silently reciting the Koran. I had faith that I would be saved by Allah. And herding cattle gave me time to contemplate. This new form of labour also gave me the opportunity to steal away into the woods to pray.[12] I felt alone, and for the first time I could enjoy peace and some small liberty to pray in the proper manner.

But I was not alone. Within a few days, I became aware of a young white boy spying on me.

'Go away,' I shouted in my own language, adding emphasis with gestures. 'Leave me alone,' I commanded.

But this brazen-faced boy, understanding the meaning if not the words, merely laughed. From then on, the encounters became far more confrontational. On many occasions whilst at my devotions, this obnoxious boy would taunt and mock me, throwing dirt in my face. In his eyes, I was the lowest of the low.

I was reduced to a state of agonising frustration, laid low by the taunts and the interruptions in my prayers. I knew that even in my weakened state I could have caught and beaten this troublesome child. But I was also deeply aware of my new position in life. I was a slave; a captive. I had no means of explaining my situation, for I remained largely ignorant of the English language. If I had retaliated, I knew I would have been severely punished.

It was then that I decided to take back my freedom and shape my own destiny.

The next morning, when I knew I was alone with the cattle, I made my escape. In truth, I had no idea where I would go or what I would do when I reached there. I knew it was a risky venture, but I was driven by the hope that I would encounter some good fortune or, at the very least, an understanding master who would take kindly to me and assist me in my quest for freedom and repatriation. I again headed into the familiar wood but, on this occasion, I did not stop to pray.

I headed across Kent Island, in the opposite direction to Annapolis, and negotiated the narrow channel that separates the island from the mainland to the east. I kept walking in this general direction through sparsely populated woods and wilderness until I reached the county of Kent, on the shores of Delaware Bay. The journey of some sixty miles over flat terrain took but a couple of days and provided me with ample refreshment – fresh water and fruit. It reminded me of some of the happy expeditions I had made back in my homeland.

While I had managed to avoid all contact with fellow humans – either native Indians, white men or black slaves – during my trek across country I was now confronted with a populated township called Dover, named after the coastal town in the county of Kent in England. I could have kept running. But it was there that I determined I would put my trust in Allah and hope to encounter an educated man who would understand my plight.

Although there were quite a few African folk walking freely about town, I could not help but notice that they displayed a curious, even suspicious, countenance. How was I to know that they were all subject to legislation, called 'For the trial of Negroes', which was far from welcoming? Under these laws there were restrictions on the number of black people who could gather together. Black people were also prevented from carrying any item that might be regarded as a weapon. The laws also laid down more severe penalties for certain crimes committed by black people than those for white people.

Much more relevant to my situation were the laws relating to runaway slaves for, apparently, it was not uncommon for captives to flee to seek their freedom. Those who aided such escapes were punished while those who arrested runaways were rewarded. A law was in force throughout the Colonies – including in Maryland and the counties bordering Delaware River and Delaware Bay[13] – that stipulated any runaway servant or slave who was not known or had no pass may be arrested by any person and kept in the common jail until his or her master could redeem his possession.

This soon became my predicament because I had not ventured too far into Dover when a couple of burly men, no doubt on the lookout for runaway slaves, grabbed me in a rough manner and asked me some questions I could not understand. Eager for their reward, the men then strong-armed me in the direction of the town's jail. The building, which surprisingly also housed the local tavern, was situated in the centre of the town next to a great green space frequented by many people enjoying relaxation and mild exercise. They hardly seemed to notice me as I was roughly forced into the building. With little ceremony or formality, I was thrown into a bare cell and left alone to contemplate my fate.

Again, I was weighed down with depression, shrouded in dark foreboding. I had every reason to fear the worst. After a while my jailer attempted to engage me in conversation in a language that I could not understand. But I could tell he was intrigued, both by my own unfamiliar utterances and my appearance, which we could all agree was somewhat different from that of the normal black African slave.

It was not many days before it was evident that my captivity was becoming a topic of interest in this small community. Even some gentlemen attending sessions at the adjacent Kent County courthouse became intrigued. They wanted to learn more, and at their behest, I was taken from my jail and moved the few paces into the King George's Tavern. There they attempted to converse with me, again in their own language that I could not understand. I was even offered wine, which I refused, much to their astonishment. At last I managed to ignite a spark of recognition and common understanding when attempting to describe in writing my faith, I uttered the words 'Allah' and 'Mohammed' that seemed familiar to them.

The gentlemen talked among themselves and then parted, leaving my jailer to escort me back to my cell to ponder on this encounter. Did their interest signify a positive development or had the meeting sealed my fate to an ordeal even worse than I had experienced? I had no way of knowing.

After some days of further incarceration, an old black African slave who lived and worked in that area was brought to my cell. He was from my part of the world, speaking Wolof, a neighbouring language to mine, and one which I could understand and make myself understood. What a blessed relief.

This kindly captive, who had been given the name of Peter,[14] explained that he had been asked to speak to me at the behest of the gentlemen whom I had met a few days earlier. The relief and excitement I felt were almost overwhelming. At last I could express my feelings to someone who could understand me.

'I want to go home. I need to go home,' were the first words that I spoke.

'But this is now your home,' said Peter. 'I am afraid you will learn that for people like us, there is no going back.'

I brushed away this response. 'That's impossible. I have family – a whole community – in Bondu who rely on me.'

'You do not understand,' Peter continued to explain in a fatherly manner. 'You are now part of the future of this young land. I have been here many, many years,' he continued. 'I have been granted many freedoms and, in my own small way, earned the respect of my fellow men, both black and white.

But I know that I will never again see my homeland, or my family and friends. That is not the way of this world.'

Peter could see in my face the impact of this news and quickly interrupted my silent protestations. 'Be aware, you are in serious trouble, my friend.'

He gently explained that under the law there were harsh penalties for runaway slaves, as well as rewards for those who captured them. As one of those runaways found more than ten miles from my master's property, I was liable to be flogged with ten lashes on my bare back.

I again protested. 'They can't do this to me. I should never have been brought here. I should never have been made a slave. You must surely understand.'

Grateful for the opportunity to unburden myself, I then told the story of how I had been captured and shipped to Maryland, of how I had fled from Mr Tolson's plantation and how I had ended up in this jail. I felt it was also important to explain my heritage, as well as my religious and trading activities.

Peter listened intently, without interruption. And when I had finished, he smiled, saying, 'Be assured, I will pass all this information on to Mr Bluett, a good man of the church and legal learning. For it was he who was among the gentlemen who met you a few days ago. He asked me to see you this day and gather information about your plight. You are fortunate, my friend, for Mr Bluett recognised there was something special about you.'

And with these reassuring words ringing in my ears, we parted. Allah had been merciful indeed.

In time I would learn that Thomas Bluett was an attorney practising in Kent County. He had also been ordained as a minister. Having been trained for the ministry in England, he had returned to Kent County to head a mission maintained by the Society for the Propagation of the Gospel. This man, of ample stomach and ruddy complexion with a clear fondness for drink, would soon become a trusted friend and in many ways my saviour.

Some four years later, in 1734, Mr Bluett a convivial, perceptive man, would record his first impression on meeting me. He wrote in his short account of my life:

> *'Upon our talking and making signs to him, he wrote a line or two before us, and when he read it, pronounced the words Allah and Mohammed; by which, and his refusing a glass of wine we offered him, we perceived he was a Mohammedan, but could not imagine of what country he was or how he got thither, for by his affable carriage and the easy composure of his countenance, we could see he was no common slave.'*

By all good fortune and in such troubling circumstances, I had at last been recognised as no common slave!

I suppose that following my meeting in jail with Peter, that most kindly of Wolof freed slaves, I had hoped to be set free there and then. But that was not the law of the land. I was still a bonded slave, in the ownership of my master, Mr Tolson.

Thanks to the information passed on by Peter to my jailer and others of influence, I was spared the ignominy of a court appearance and punishment inflicted on runaway slaves. It was not long before Mr Tolson sent two of his men to accompany me back to the plantation in Queen Anne's County.

My arrival in Chesapeake Bay was far different from my first encounter, however. Mr Tolson treated me with great courtesy. Although we could still not understand each other, it was clear that he had heeded what he had learnt from my conversation with Peter. I was allocated my own hut and allowed the privilege of praying there in private whenever I needed.

'Thank you,' I said hesitantly, for these were two of the few English words that I had learnt from Peter.

My task – still tending the cattle – was never unreasonable. Now, however, my master seemed intent on making my enslavement as easy as possible.

'Thank you,' I repeated at every display of kindness shown to me.

But this was still an alien life. I knew I could never content myself with this existence. Following a good deal of gesticulating to my master, and many more expressions of gratitude, I managed to secure the permission and means to write a letter in Arabic to my father, relaying all that had happened to me and seeking his help in gaining my release and return to Africa.

'There is no good in the country of the Christians for a Muslim,' I wrote, perhaps somewhat harshly. I announced to all the Muslim men and women of Bondu that I was alive, having been taken to the land of the Christians 'across the great sea'. I appealed to the rulers of my homeland and my family to ensure that my wives did not remarry.

With the help of others more skilled in languages, this letter was then addressed in both English and French: 'To Mr Solomon, the son of Abraham, Priest at Bondu, near Maccana in Foutre up the River Senegal in Africa.'

The message was then carried to Vachel Denton, who clearly held an important position in Annapolis. Instructions were given for the letter to be carried to Africa by Capt. Pike.

I thought that the transmission of my message would be a reasonably simple affair. Unfortunately, it proved to be anything but. As I learnt later, Capt. Pike had already set sail to London when Mr Denton took possession of the letter, so he enclosed it in a packet and sent it instead on another ship, this time addressed to Capt. Hunt in London. The packet included instructions for my letter to be passed to Capt. Pike, so it could be carried on the final leg of the triangular trade route back to my father in Africa.

While the letter was carried across the Atlantic without a problem, it arrived in London too late to reach Capt. Pike, who had already sailed for the Gambia. Capt. Hunt was in a quandary. He had another ship about to sail to the Gambia, which he could have used for the dispatch but, unable to read my message or judge its importance, he decided to seek the opinion of an acquaintance. Capt. Hunt turned to a ship chandler, in Wapping – Joseph Ames, a noted antiquary and an expert on books. Mr Ames then took a copy of the letter to have it translated. At the same time, Capt. Hunt also consulted his friends in the Royal African Company. Notable among these associates was James Oglethorpe, the Deputy Governor of the company. Mr Oglethorpe had established a strong reputation as a soldier, Member of Parliament and philanthropist, and was someone who really cared about the plight of people less fortunate than himself, most notably the poor unfortunate people who found themselves in debtors' prisons.

No doubt intrigued by my letter and the story behind its transmission, Mr Oglethorpe decided that he too would have the message translated. He sent the letter to Professor John Gagnier, a French-born orientalist, who held the Laudian Chair of Arabic at Oxford University. By all accounts, when the letter was returned, and Mr Oglethorpe was able to read for himself the unwarranted hardships that had descended on me, he was greatly moved and had no hesitation in deciding that my slavery was unjust and that I should be freed.

I was truly blessed, for there was probably no Englishman

better placed or more influential as a humanitarian who could have secured my freedom. And yet this was but the first of many instances in which one of England's most important people would come to my aid.

In June 1732 – a full year after my incarceration in the Kent County jail – Mr Oglethorpe gave his bond for the payment of forty-five pounds to have me freed and delivered to him in London. The deal was agreed with Capt. Henry Hunt who, in turn, arranged to use the offices of Vachel Denton, his agent in Maryland, to expedite the transaction. Instructions were then sent on the next ship to Annapolis, where my master readily agreed my sale at the original purchase price, almost certainly pleased to be relieved of my unsatisfactory labours.

Mr Tolson shook my hands firmly and spoke warm words in English that I could still not fully understand, but I like to think were along the lines of 'I wish you well'.

I was now a free man, staying as a guest of Mr Denton and his wife Anne in their fine house on the corner of Prince George Street and Maryland Avenue in Annapolis, anxious to start my journey away from this cold continent. But I was going nowhere. Winter had set in with a vengeance.

The seasonal bitterness that I had already endured once had frozen hard the rivers and estuaries of Maryland, making them impassable to shipping. I was fortunate to be given multiple layers of thick clothing to wear. Even so, I knew then that I would never grow to enjoy really cold weather, however much the snow transformed the earth to such innocent whiteness.

I concede it was heart-warming to see excited children throwing themselves into piles of snow and gleefully tossing balls of the compressed powder at each other and, if they were brave, sliding down icy inclines at a furious speed. They were not alone, for adults seemed happy to join in the fun, to relive their childhood.

I enjoyed the unfamiliar experience of tramping through drifts of whiteness, making squeaking impressions and leaving pristine footprints as though I was an intrepid explorer in this far-off land. It was enchanting; so very different. But I was always happy to return to the warmth of my lodgings.

Mr and Mrs Denton were generous and thoughtful hosts. For the first time I was experiencing life in a well-lit Western household with all the modern comforts of affluent white people and I felt cocooned in the warmth of their hospitality. I was fortified by good wholesome food, thoughtfully provided in accordance with my religious principles, and kept warm by fires in the hearth and appropriate clothing.

The room provided for my rest, prayers and sleeping was equipped with a bed, raised above the floor, that was so wonderfully soft and covered with many blankets. This was in such contrast to the rudimentary bed of my home and the uncomfortable sleeping arrangements of my slave hut and jail. Even my most private functions were cared for with the provision of a chamber pot that was thoughtfully emptied by servants of the household.

I am now ashamed to relate that despite this comfort and hospitality, my early days with the Dentons were still troubled by a feeling of frustration. I could not help but feel trapped, almost enslaved, against my free will. But as time went by, I developed a more positive, relaxed countenance.

In many ways it was a surreal experience, for slaves working in Mr Denton's household were the ones who usually served me my food, and often saw to my welfare and comfort. These black servants, men and women, who I must say seemed reasonably content with their lot, were just some of the sizeable slave labour force that Mr Denton had working for him on his properties. It appeared that he was conscious of his position in society and his responsibility for setting a good example among the community of slave owners. During my stay I saw little by way of ill treatment among his people, but a good deal of kindness.

Like Mr Oglethorpe, Mr Denton was a man of great influence. Born in Maryland, he was an attorney who had risen to be a city alderman, Mayor of Annapolis and a member of the Maryland parliament, the General Assembly, representing Annapolis in the Lower House from 1725 to 1727. (In later years he regained his place to represent Anne Arundel County.)

Mr Denton was also a religious man, serving for some time as a vestryman at St Anne's Episcopal Church. Maybe this was why he was so tolerant, even supportive, of me as I fulfilled my own obligations, including praying and quietly reciting the Koran. It was in this supportive environment that I began to learn my first words of English, partly by listening intently to conversations around me. Here I was greatly helped by Mr and Mrs Denton and their household slaves, as well as their many acquaintances, two in particular.

One was the Rev. Jacob Henderson, an Irish clergyman and a gentleman of great knowledge. Having emigrated to these parts in 1710, he served the religious communities of both Dover and St Anne's Parish in Annapolis. The Rev. Henderson and his wife, Mary, even built a small chapel, known as Henderson's Chapel, at nearby Belair. The high esteem in which he was held within the church led him to being appointed Commissary to the Bishop of London, a position which meant he convened the Conventions of the Clergy on both the western and eastern shores of the province. It so happened that the Rev. Henderson was also well-acquainted with Mr Denton, who had served as a vestryman at St Anne's Church in Annapolis.

On a personal note, I found that the Rev. Henderson and I had much in common, sharing a life of piety and learning.

I came to realise that he was not universally popular among the clergy as he often challenged their profligacy and lack of discipline. This met with a good deal of resistance which, I later learnt, led to him resigning his position by 1734.

The other clergyman of influence was the Rev. John Humphreys, Rector of St Anne's Church in Annapolis, a position previously held by the Rev. Henderson. The Rev. Humphreys also regularly said prayers and read the Christian Divine Service at the proceedings of the Maryland General Assembly. He, too, was a man of great learning. We spent a good deal of time together, with him helping me with my English and me trying my best to teach him rudimentary Arabic.

During our conversations, I tried to explain what I was feeling within my heart – that I regarded my fate much like Joseph of Nazareth, who was forced to travel afar into strange lands. I felt emboldened to share my innermost thought: that it was God's will that I should be sold into slavery so that I could improve myself and better understand distant cultures.

At last the winter relented and in March 1733 I eagerly prepared myself for the voyage to England. The ship that was to carry me was the *William*, under the command of Capt. George Uriell, a kindly man from Maryland's Anne Arundel County, who greeted me warmly. There would be no slaves confined below on this leg of the triangular trans-Atlantic trade.

Although I was still a captive, under the authority of Capt. Henry Hunt, my consignee, the conditions awaiting me on board were far different from those that I suffered on the voyage from the Gambia. I was given my own quarters, admittedly somewhat cramped, where I had privacy to think and pray. I was also pleased to see that among the passengers boarding the *William* was none other than Mr Bluett, whom

I had first met when I was in such distressed circumstances in the Kent County jailhouse.

This time I was able to express my greetings and relief in a few words of English – albeit they were said hesitantly and in a manner which still left Mr Bluett somewhat bemused.

'I am happy, and I am thankful,' was what I tried to say.

CHAPTER 4

A new life in England

◇◇◇

The voyage to England took just six weeks. It should have been a pleasant contrast to my previous passage when I was being brutally treated as a slave. This time I sailed in modest comfort, well-fed and clothed in appropriate attire, thanks again to the generosity of Mr Denton. Unfortunately, the weather was foul for almost the entire journey. The winds may have been favourable, making for a speedy passage, but the hostility of the seas and the pitching and tossing of our vessel meant I was sick for much of the time.

Fortunately, Mr Bluett and the attentive captain took great care of me, doing their best to keep me preoccupied by teaching me English. Gradually I became familiar with the alphabet and the more commonly used words and expressions in their language. As the weeks went by, I was able to understand more and more of what was being said to me and, perhaps even more remarkable, able to express myself in a manner that, for the most part, they could understand. Mr Bluett proved to be a remarkable teacher. He remained patient and diligent even though I know he, too, was suffering from the effects of the ship's motion.

Capt. Uriell and his crew were also kind to me all the time I was in their care. While they seemed to relish the harsh sailing conditions, they were understanding of my weakness. They were also most tolerant of my religious devotions which must have seemed strange to them. Early in the voyage they came to understand that I was not permitted to eat pork – a popular item in their diet. I even managed to make them understand some of the fundamentals of my faith, and in those moments when my stomach seemed settled, I was permitted to kill poultry and other animals needed for fresh meat.

As we approached the shores of England, with the weather and sea state adopting a much calmer attitude, it was noticeable how the mood of the whole crew lightened. At times they became boisterous and excitable, for they were nearing home. I was touched and somewhat surprised to be included in their celebrations and even more delighted as they tested my new linguistic skills by pointing out landmarks and places of interest as we sailed up the English Channel.

I carefully noted down this information so that if I met an Englishman on my return to Africa, I could impress him with my knowledge of his country and, hopefully, convince him that I had truly been to England. For I was still determined that this voyage in the *William* would be but a prelude to another, back to my beloved Africa where I belonged.

It was a fine, warm morning that day on Thursday, May 3, 1733 as we entered the mighty Thames Estuary and then rode the tide westwards towards the heart of London; a great city which I knew only from reputation. My sense of wonderment heightened with every passing hour.

The sight of many ships jostling for space and headway was not new to me. I had seen this spectacle in the entrance of the River Gambia, in Maryland, and in the English Channel as we approached this destination. But I had witnessed nothing that compared with the spectacle before me.

The River Thames seemed to be crammed full of vessels of all sizes and purpose. Some were huddled alongside the banks, in places nestling against wharves. Others were anchored in the deeper water of the tidal river basins. There were so many that some ships seemed to be locked together, as if in some great maritime battle. And wherever you looked there were smaller sailing barges, ferries and row boats flitting hither and thither, fetching, carrying and delivering goods and people to myriad destinations. All this left my eyes dazzled and my mind confused.

I also found it hard to comprehend the form and structure in the huddle of buildings, large and small and of all shapes, sizes and purpose. The mass of people, all going about their daily business and graft, was bewildering to my eyes so unaccustomed to such frantic activity. And the stench to my naive senses was overwhelming, as if great vats of human waste had been mixed with sweet-smelling fruits and spices of far-off lands.

Captain Uriell demonstrated great skill as he brought our ship to anchor in a deep-water basin, ready to offload the cargo into waiting barges. I was told that the cargo would be checked by customs at the Legal Quays, close to London Bridge, before being taken to warehouses. As for me, I waited to be taken ashore by a small boat, all the while eagerly scanning the shore for sight of some welcoming party. I was especially looking forward to meeting the great Mr Oglethorpe who had bought my freedom.

But when I reached dry land, I found there was no

gathering of well-wishers on the dockside; only Capt. Hunt. He told us that Mr Oglethorpe no longer resided in London. Several months earlier, having retired from the Royal African Company, Mr Oglethorpe had set sail to cross the Atlantic to help establish a new British Colony in Georgia. Mr Bluett, who thankfully remained at my side during disembarkation, explained that as Mr Oglethorpe had not been able to complete the transaction to redeem his bond, I was still in the ownership of Capt. Hunt. I was still a slave!

Not that I was shackled in chains or forced into some hovel to again lead a life of servitude. Instead, Capt. Hunt and Mr Bluett took me to nearby lodgings with a family on the waterfront in Limehouse, to the east of London, not far from the docks.[15] There I was provided with food and clothing and allowed to wander and explore as I pleased.

At first all seemed well with my lot. My lodgings were exceedingly comfortable, being the home of a merchant, who I assumed had connections in the Royal African Company, his family and several servants. The well-constructed house was made of bricks, with many windows, and situated in appropriately named Narrow Street. This house backed on to the north side of the River Thames, which meant the senses were assaulted by the various sounds, noises and smells of maritime activities – ships and boats being built and repaired and loaded and unloaded with so many different cargoes. Many of the shoreline buildings – modest homes, workshops and warehouses – seemed to be built on top of each other, so I was not surprised when I was told a few weeks into my stay that there had been a great fire in Limehouse in 1717 when some 150 houses were destroyed by fire.

My stay in Limehouse was made especially pleasurable by my hosts, a hospitable and caring family that included a not-unattractive daughter who was late in her schooling.

Many a shy glance was exchanged, for both of us were taken by our contrasting appearance: she with her grey-blue eyes and fair hair, and me of distinctive African countenance with tawny skin and crinkly hair. But what pleased me most was the understanding and tolerance shown by my hosts to my religious devotions and adherence to Islamic dietary laws, all of which must have been unfamiliar to them.

In these early weeks I spent much time in my room, in prayer and quiet contemplation. I felt driven to write down from memory a complete copy of the Koran as a pious act of discipline and thanksgiving for my freedom from slavery. This became an all-consuming occupation, for in the following months not only did I manage to make one copy, I was inspired to make two more, each written from memory and without the need for me to so much as look at the previously written versions.

Thanks to the donation of my hosts and other new acquaintances, I was fortunate to assemble a great many sheets of paper of various types and thickness on which to write the recalled text of the Koran. Many of these sheets had been designed for bookkeeping and some even had entries, including one with the name of William Hunt, the London merchant who worked closely with Vachel Denton of Maryland and was thus involved in securing my freedom.

The pile of paper that I had gathered was invaluable, as each copy of the Koran was made up of about 440 pages of Arabic text set down in my hand. I found it so satisfying, and uplifting, to see the verses I remembered taking shape on the page, although I regret the writing was not of the neatest quality. In my younger life I had limited need for writing as our teachings, messages and instructions were usually passed by word of mouth, by song or drumbeat. At home, when there was a need to set down text in the written form, I used a traditional pen made from a reed, which was so much easier to make the contrast between thick and thin strokes than the quill pens provided for my use in England.

I confess that I found it much more difficult to express myself in the written Arabic form when I was not reiterating text that I had learnt from memory. The messages that I felt compelled to write as an introduction to the Korans almost certainly betrayed my lack of education in Arabic composition. With no-one around me to guide or correct such writing, I had no alternative but to set down my thoughts in the best way I could.[16]

First, I described a little about myself and my family, listing the names of the Twelve Apostles and providing an explanation – based on the words of the Koran itself – that in setting down the text I had no intention of forging the words of God. Whatever its imperfections, I felt that I had achieved something worthwhile, demonstrating my faith in this country of Christians.

While I spent many of my early days in Limehouse confined in my own room, I gradually gained confidence and became increasingly inquisitive. Fortunately, I was encouraged to venture outside into my neighbouring surroundings. My hosts were keen to show off a Christian church – St Anne's – that only recently had been built close by, a little away from the waterfront. It was certainly impressive, requiring money raised from a tax on coal imports for its construction.

The striking feature of this large church, constructed in gleaming white stone, was the tall, imposing tower. I spotted a flag flying from a pole on top of the tower. It was the white ensign, a flag that I had seen before being displayed on British naval ships as we approached and entered the English Channel.[17] It was explained that a previous monarch, the late Queen Anne, had decreed that the ensign should be flown. As a result, the tower and flag had already become established as a marker for seafarers seeking their bearings.

I was pleased to see this church having some practical use as a landmark, for I must admit I found it hard to comprehend why so much money and effort had been expended on establishing such a grand place for the pious act of worship. Who, I wondered, were the builders trying to impress? Surely not God.

Another place where I felt uneasy, even though I could better understand its purpose and attraction, was The Grapes tavern, a dark, narrow establishment situated between Narrow Street and the river, but a few steps from my lodgings. The tavern was crowded as working people and women of uncertain background refreshed themselves and sheltered from the intense heat of the sun.

My arrival in England had coincided with one of the hottest summers in memory. While I felt quite at home in this climate, it was clear that many people were feeling uncomfortable and even distressed. I had been taken inside the tavern for 'education' and refreshment although I was not tempted to partake of the strong liquor that seemed to be having such a devastating impact on the senses of the drinkers. I was no stranger to the effects of liquor, for I had witnessed many a bout of intoxication in my African homeland.

On several occasions I was taken to the city by a small boat, called a wherry, rowed by tough, hardened watermen who knew much about the waterfront and the vagaries of the fast-flowing River Thames. We reached these boats by means of stone steps that were near my lodgings. These watermen's stairs, leading down from street level, could be exceedingly slippery and treacherous – but then I was used to boarding small boats in hazardous conditions on rivers like the Gambia and Faleme back in Africa.

During our river journey upstream, the watermen would often shout out features of some of the main buildings and structures along the way. I was particularly struck by the sight of the imposing – and forbidding – Tower of London that had clearly established such a prominent role in England's history. Then there was the impressive, and to my eyes peculiar, London Bridge – a structure of many stone arches upon which had been built many shops and houses of varying design and maintenance. It was an awesome sight, made that much more memorable by all the people, horses, carts, and carriages negotiating the crossing between the buildings.

Never have I seen such a melee. I was told that the crowds and congestion had become so bad that a few years previously it had been decreed that travellers should be separated, with those moving from the City to the southern side of the Thames keeping to the east side of the bridge and those heading towards the City moving on the other side.

While in benign tidal conditions it was possible for the watermen to carry us beneath the bridge and onward into heart of London, on several occasions we were forced to leave the boat downstream and walk on or rejoin our boat on the upstream side. The flow of the river, together with constrictions of the stone arches, combined to turn the water into hazardous rapids that only the most skilful boatmen could negotiate. As I was once told by one of the watermen, there was an old saying that the bridge was for wise men to pass over and for fools to pass under.

Sometimes I would explore alone, often walking a few miles westwards to London proper, each time negotiating my way through the jumble of buildings and workplaces while doing my best to avoid the throngs of people, animals and vehicles of all descriptions that populated this urban jungle. I must admit it was an uncomfortable experience as wherever

I walked, I was met with quizzical, and sometimes hostile, stares and glances.

Not that I was alone in being from a foreign land. I was surprised to see a good number of black people, invariably dressed in poor quality clothing as worn by the English labouring classes, walking freely through the lanes and alleyways. It was explained to me that while seemingly free, these negroes had been brought to England as servants to planters and traders returning home from the Americas and the Caribbean. Most commonly they were unpaid and disciplined and punished without impunity.

In contrast, thanks to Capt. Hunt and Mr Bluett on his infrequent visits, I was able to begin building up a small community of acquaintances, some of whom would soon become the nucleus of influential friends. And all the time I was improving my ability to speak and understand the English language.

But throughout this time, I was consumed by a major concern. Although I was content with the welcome and hospitality shown to me, I could not avoid being worried about my true freedom. I was still a slave. My future, my prospects and my ability to return to my family in Africa remained out of my hands.

I would have been even more concerned – probably desolate – if I knew then what I now know to be my true position, according to legal opinion. In 1729, the Attorney and Solicitor General had ruled that slaves who had been moved from the West Indies to Great Britain, with or without their master, remained their masters' property, even if they had become Christian by being baptised. Until then it had been widely assumed that a Christian could not be a slave. While I had not returned from the West Indies, I would probably have found if difficult in the extreme to argue for my freedom, even if I had taken the unthinkable precautionary step of being baptised as a Christian.

My anxiety grew when one of my new acquaintances told me that some persons had contacted Capt. Hunt with an offer to buy me. Apparently, they were making out that the purchase would enable me to return home, but the suspicion was they would either sell me on as a slave or demand an unreasonable ransom for me to be returned to Africa.

I was distraught and mightily relieved to see Mr Bluett arrive at my lodgings. Concerned about my anxieties, my good friend immediately took me to London with him. He then sought the permission of Capt. Hunt to let me accompany him on a visit to his home on the Theobalds Estate in Cheshunt, a pleasant village on the River Lea in Hertfordshire to the north of London.

On our arrival, following an uneventful journey by carriage, Mr Bluett explained that there was once a great palace – one of the finest in England – set in this parkland. For 100 years or so Theobalds was the setting for great meetings of state, intrigues and plots, as well as entertainment and hunting. Two of this country's monarchs, James I and his son Charles I, adopted Theobalds as a Royal Palace, with King James I even establishing a menagerie in the estate where he introduced many exotic animals.

No doubt some of the many animals had been shipped from Africa, for there were elephants and camels among the wide variety of wildlife introduced into this corner of England. And here, these birds and animals were kept in this strange environment in the confines of captivity at great expense and trouble. I smiled ruefully, thinking how this King, with all his riches, was trying to recreate the landscape of my homeland, where magnificent beasts and exotic birds such as flamingos, pelicans and kingfishers enjoyed their freedom in the most natural of surroundings. Had not I also been brought to this unfamiliar land in such circumstances?

Those animals had long gone when I visited. So too had that magnificent palace, which was demolished in the mid-1600s, with part of the ruins being incorporated into the modern homes built in this estate. And it was here that concern about my own captivity was eased somewhat by news imparted by Mr Bluett.

He confirmed what I had heard, that Capt. Hunt had been approached by someone willing to buy me, perhaps to send me home with a ransom or even sell me on as a slave. Capt. Hunt had replied he would not part with me without my consent. However, given that Mr Oglethorpe was out of the country, the good captain might be willing to sell me to any of my friends if they undertook to help me return home to Africa, according to my wishes. Whatever transpired, no action would be taken without Mr Bluett being informed.

While residing with my legal friend in Cheshunt, I had the honour of being introduced to many of the educated gentry of that place. Quite a few wealthy London merchants had chosen this area for their country homes, conveniently close – just fifteen miles – north of the capital. These gentlemen were most welcoming and quite concerned with my misfortunes. Their generosity was palpable, for I was given several handsome presents. Led by Mr Bluett, I believe, these good men even talked of making a subscription to a fund to purchase my freedom.

In the end this generosity was not needed because steps were being taken to purchase my freedom in another place. It transpired that on my arrival in London, Capt. Hunt had immediately informed the Royal African Company and offered to make a tender of me to the company at forty-five pounds on the same terms as Mr Oglethorpe's bond. This had been reported to the Court of Assistants, a committee of the company's governing body, on May 3, shortly after my ship had docked in London.

The court agreed that in Mr Oglethorpe's absence they would take up the offer, given that I might well be of service to the company once I had gained my freedom and allowed to return to the Gambia. By all accounts, members of the court felt that my assistance might be especially useful given that I understood and, more importantly, could write Arabic.

I took some pleasure in the way my agreeable new acquaintances flattered me. They repeatedly complimented me about the way I was adapting to this new way of life and the way my facility with English was improving. As indeed it was.

I also appreciated the way in which they happily demonstrated the workings that lay within the machines, tools and appliances which brought them pleasure and eased their burden of labour. They seemed impressed with the way I could reassemble, unaided and without a word of instruction, a clock or some other instrument that had been taken apart for my interest. I relished the challenge of reassembling farm implements, including a plough and a grist mill used for grinding grain into flour.

'How do you do that?' they asked, as if such tasks should have been beyond my comprehension.

'Easy,' I replied. 'It's just a matter of memory and common sense,' I added, happy to have demonstrated that such skills were not reserved for white people alone.

I have no doubt these good people were misinterpreting the true purpose of my interest and enquiry. They might well have been thinking that I was anxious to become more like them; eager to adapt my 'primitive' lifestyle into the ways of sophisticated Western society. They could not have been more mistaken.

In truth, like the squirrels that I had studied scampering around their estates, I was engaged in a process of gathering and storing. I had started a process of collecting ideas, ways of working and other aspects of this more-developed society that might be introduced into my community back home. But I was certain that nothing in this so-called modern world would change the fundamental beliefs, values and lifestyle that I still cherished. I had every intention of returning to the warmth of Africa, of being with my family and resuming my life in the familiar, natural surroundings that were truly part of my soul. And, quietly, I yearned to return very soon.

CHAPTER 5

Rise to the top of the social elite

My experiences during the following months remain in my memory for two main reasons. The first concerned the way that the gentlemen in society, including leading men of letters and successful businessmen, increasingly accepted me as one of their own. However, in truth I was still very conscious that I differed greatly in appearance, and my command of the English language was still far from being fluent or adequately descriptive. That said, I was often encouraged to retell stories of my homeland.

One tale in particular seemed to capture my hosts' imagination. It concerned the day when I and four of my servants were travelling through the countryside – an area under the rule of Arab leaders – with a group of black African captives. Suddenly we were set upon by some fifteen wild men from a neighbouring Arab tribe. With one of my servants left to guard our captives, I joined the other three to fight off the aggressors. We were successful, although sadly one of my men was killed and I was run through the leg with a spear. The aggressors fared much worse, for we managed to kill their leader and two others, as well as two horses, before they fled.

Often my hosts would remark that they were surprised to hear such a story being told by a man they considered to be of mild and reserved countenance; a man of religion. Although many of my new companions were well-travelled, they really had no concept of the harsh realities of life in Africa.

The other matter that was exercising my mind during this period concerned my status. I was aware that while I was living freely, accepted and moving at will among this growing group of influential friends and acquaintances, I was still captive; still a slave. While my bond remained in the ownership of Capt. Hunt, I remained at risk from being returned to harsh work, or perhaps even worse, I might be sold on at an extravagant profit to a new, unscrupulous owner. In my own mind, I could imagine my value being enhanced by the rising social status and newly acquired language skills that they themselves were encouraging.

While I privately considered ways of extricating myself from these bonds, I continued the social round of meetings, telling stories of my heritage, reciting from memory verses of the Koran and learning as much as possible about the way of life in this new-found society. I was fortunate to be mixing with such interesting and erudite men... and women too, some of whom I must admit were both agreeable in countenance and pleasing on the eye.

I now find it difficult to recall the names of all those I met – in their homes, places of work and in London coffeehouses – during 1733, this year of intense socialising. But one person I do remember with the greatest of affection was Joseph Smith, a wholesale grocer, who lived under the sign of The Sugar Loaf, in Cannon Street.

It was during one of my early walks from Limehouse into London proper that I had encountered Joseph in Cannon Street, some three miles east – almost in a straight line – from my lodgings. I had stopped to admire the array of fruit, vegetables and other groceries on display when Joseph came forward and, recognising that I was not English, offered me an apple. It was an act of friendly generosity that I have never forgotten.

Joseph was a kindly man and yet quite unlike the many grand and learned gentlemen who would later welcome me into their company. Very quickly we established a routine of meeting at his home, at times almost weekly, even during a time, much later, when I lodged in African House. Fortunately, this building, the headquarters of the Royal African Company, was in Leadenhall Street, close by Cannon Street.

A tradesman with few airs and graces, Joseph made his living by supplying groceries to shops and grand houses throughout London and its surrounding communities. Towards the end of our initial encounter he answered a question that had intrigued me for much of our meeting. What was the significance of the sugar loaf, depicted above the entrance of his premises?

'The sugar loaf is what we call the conical cake of refined sugar that we sell, in this handy form, to our customers,' he explained. 'Sugar is one of our main products that we sell, along with fruit and vegetables.'

Joseph told me that his supply of loaves came from small refineries, close by, just south of Cannon Street, where the sugar was boiled and solidified.'

'Of course,' he added, 'we, in this country, would not have such a thriving sugar business without the help of African slaves working in the cane fields in the Americas and Caribbean.'

I felt compelled to reply, as best I could in my halting

English: 'You could say the same about the tobacco business as well, as I know from my own painful experience. But you are wrong to imply that slaves are helping. They are driven to labour, often in the most tortuous of circumstances, and always against their will. The trade, as I have experienced it, has few virtues for those enslaved.' My command of English did not allow me to be so precise or eloquent in my protest, but my feelings and sentiment were made plain. And they were evidently understood.

This was the first time in my short time in England I had been so emboldened to speak in this manner. But it was to Joseph's credit that he listened without interruption or challenge. By great fortune, I had chosen my audience wisely, for from that moment on, Joseph and I had many open discussions, always conducted in the politest of manners, concerning the rights and wrongs of the slave trade. It must be said that while we came from different ends of the arguments, neither of us could say we were wholly for or against slavery. That was probably why we found our companionship so easy.

Joseph taught me much about the art of trading, of keeping and presenting produce in the most attractive way and of making sure that he always turned a profit. Even the produce that had lingered well past its prime time was sold for a few pence to the poorer people in society. But Joseph was a kindly, Christian man whom I often saw give away surplus fruit and vegetables to the most destitute.

He was also inquisitive, eager to hear about my experiences of growing and preparing food in my homeland, and I was always happy to answer as best I could. I was pleased that he displayed a keen interest in my faith and traditions, and I came to appreciate how willing he was to share his knowledge. I learnt much about the habits – especially the eating habits – of the English people, and how they varied depending on their wealth and position in society. It was Joseph, more than any other I met, who opened my eyes fully to the great disparity between the rich and poor in this country.

In many ways it was my conversations with Joseph that showed how fortunate I was to be guided through this unfamiliar social labyrinth by such a good and diligent friend as Mr Bluett. Others who were especially instrumental in opening doors were George Sale, an orientalist and solicitor who was a prominent member of the Society for the Promotion of Christian Knowledge; and Sir Hans Sloane, a noted physician, naturalist and probably the greatest collector of rarities of his time. Each of these three made a great impression on me and provided experiences and memories that have remained with me throughout my life.

George Sale, for instance, had acquired a deep knowledge of the Arabic language and customs, having spent many years in Arabia. Consequently, our conversations and quest for new knowledge were greatly helped by the ease of discourse in both English and Arabic. Our meetings were always stimulating, and I am so grateful that he sought me out so early after my arrival in London. On our initial meeting, I explained to him that as part of my learning in my youth back in Bondu, I used to read the Arabic translation of the New Testament issued by the Society for the Promotion of Christian Knowledge.

'Well I never,' exclaimed Mr Sale. 'What a coincidence. I worked on that translation.'

It transpired that he had been a corrector for the translation, issued back in 1726. He then told me that he was now working on a translation of the Koran. Indeed, it was nearing completion – including genealogical charts, a map of Arabia, and extensive notes about Eastern traditions, manners and laws. This ambitious work, the first to translate directly from the Arabic into English, was published the following year, in 1734.

Like Mr Sale, it seems, Sir Hans Sloane had also been eager to make my acquaintance, once my place among London's intellectual society had begun to be established. I have no doubt that I appealed to his natural curiosity, for he was a man who thirsted for knowledge, new experiences and fresh ideas, all of which seemed to be reflected in his superior countenance.

While I was always treated with courtesy and not once made to feel inferior, I must admit I was somewhat in awe of Sir Hans. He was an imposing man in his seventies, and he had accumulated considerable wealth, thanks in part to his practice as a physician to the rich and famous, including three successive sovereigns: Queen Anne, King George I and King George II. Throughout his life he had added to his wealth through shrewd property investments, including the purchase in 1713 of the manor of Chelsea, which provided the grounds for the Apothecaries' Garden.[18] Sir Hans had a great love of the garden dating back to the 1680s, when as a trainee physician he had studied there. So, in 1722 he leased the garden to the Apothecaries for five pounds a year in perpetuity, on the condition that annually they submitted the dried specimen of fifty of their herbs to the Royal Society.

Substantial income was also derived by Sir Hans from his interest in Jamaican sugar plantations tended by the enforced labour of black African slaves whom he considered to be 'a very perverse generation of people'. Who knows, I might well have provided several captives to this very enterprise! The great collector had even assembled curiosities related to slavery, including a bullet used by a runaway slave in Jamaica, a manatee strap used for whipping slaves in West India plantations and the coat of a rebellious runaway slave who lived in the woods of Jamaica. I secretly wondered whether he was hoping that I might provide him with some such souvenir.

The careers of each of these great men would have provided an ample basis for discussion and perhaps argument, but it was Sir Hans's thirst for knowledge and his interest in the natural world that inspired me most and provided the catalyst for a most rewarding relationship. Here was this great man, a pillar of the Royal Society and an extraordinary collector, seeking my opinions and information from my background, as well as my assistance as a translator.

I was to learn much later that following our meetings he wrote a letter to an acquaintance describing me as 'a native of the inward parts of Africa, a black Mahometan priest who had great knowledge of the Ancient as well as modern Arabick'. Sir Hans went on to explain that I had been a slave in 'Pensylvania' and that, being discovered to be a scholar and unable to labour as a slave, I had my freedom given back to me.

Among the collection of over 40,000 specimens from all periods of history and from all parts of the world were many medals and manuscripts in Arabic, and Sir Hans employed me on a reasonable salary to help with their translations and annotations.[19] I spent many happy hours immersed in this worthwhile activity in Sir Hans's London home: two adjoining, and extremely impressive, residences in Great Russell Street. The home was situated in an area known as Bloomsbury. It was a pleasant place with fresh, clean air, a contrast to my first experience of wandering through some of the unsavoury parts of London.

Sir Hans's houses were packed with most of his extensive collection. But they were both his place of residence where he followed a domestic routine, invariably rising early at six in the morning, and a place where, from the kindness of his heart, he often treated unfortunates who were sick but too poor to pay for treatment. I am aware that among those helped in this way was a black African woman who had been a slave in Jamaica and brought to England to be a house servant.

Sir Hans confided the advice he had given this poor woman. Maybe she had requested an abundant supply of medicines to cure or prevent illness.

'I advise you to do what I practise myself,' he told her. 'I never take physic when I am well, and when I am ill, I take a little and only such as has been well tried.'

The servant was well-treated, for Sir Hans also provided her with his new milk chocolate recipe – a mixture of milk, chocolate and sugar – that he had brought back from Jamaica, where he had spent two years studying plants and creatures of that island. He explained that he had prescribed this drink because 'it would be light on her stomach and good to consume'.

I was fortunate that Sir Hans also received many of his distinguished circle of friends at his home. They included none other than Joseph Ames – ship chandler and noted antiquary – who in 1731 had helped with the translation of my letter to my father. Following our formal introduction, I quickly found this man to be a most agreeable and supportive companion. Then in his mid-forties, Mr Ames resided in Wapping, on the east side of London, with his wife and daughter. I was saddened to learn that while his wife had successfully given birth to six children, only the one had survived. On the other hand, he had clearly accumulated great wealth and influence though his business in trade and his success as a collector of rare books and manuscripts as well as coins, portraits, and other rare and curious items. It is little wonder that Mr Ames and Sir Hans were such close associates.

Two others I encountered in Great Russell Street were Dr Cromwell Mortimer, Sir Hans's medical assistant; and Maurice

Johnson, who was another noted collector of antiquaries, and man of letters and influence. These new acquaintances, and others, would be among this growing circle of distinguished gentlemen who would soon be so influential in my future welfare.

I set down a little of the achievements of these men to illustrate how fortunate I was, as a stranger from African shores, a one-time slave, to be welcomed and accepted in England's intellectual society. No peer of this land could have asked for more.

Dr Mortimer had already established an enviable reputation for his medical skills by the time of our meeting in Sir Hans's home. In 1719, at the age of twenty-one, he had enrolled in the prestigious Dutch medical faculty in Leyden. Sometime after being awarded his Doctor of Medicine degree in 1724, Dr Mortimer returned to London from Continental Europe, where he had undertaken several research projects, to practise medicine in London's Hanover Square.

In 1728 the young Dr Mortimer was elected a Fellow of the Royal Society and two years later became its Secretary. I have no doubt that Sir Hans Sloane must have had some influence in these accolades. Indeed, in the following year Dr Mortimer accepted an invitation from Sir Hans to move into the Great Russell Street premises, where they could treat patients and conduct research together. It was evident that a strong bond had been established between the two men, cemented by a mutual interest and shared respect.

'You can learn much from this man,' Sir Hans once advised me, adding, 'and I have no doubt his natural inquisitiveness will extract much valuable information from you as well.'

He was right. I did, indeed, find Dr Mortimer to be fascinating and convivial company, especially when he described his interest in poisons, from the points of view of both chemist and doctor. It was a subject that also interested me.

In quite recent times Dr Mortimer had examined the dangerous practice of using laurel leaves for food flavouring. Using dogs in his experiments, he had shown that the distilled extract of laurel leaves was a very strong poison 'equally mortal with the bite of a rattle snake.' The discovery was extremely important because laurel leaves and berries were often used to add flavour to creams, puddings and cordials. As he wrote in a published paper on the subject, 'the use of these liquors must certainly be exceeding prejudicial and unwholesome, and in weakly persons must hasten death.' Sadly, this observation proved to be all too true, for a doctor in Dublin wrote to Dr Mortimer informing him that two women had died after consuming distilled water of laurel leaves.

During one of our meetings, the doctor also told me he was also beginning to take an interest in a possible treatment for people bitten by the poisonous viper, or adder, a snake which is to be found in England. This treatment, it seems, involved the application of some form of salad oil.

Dr Mortimer, like so many others I met during my time in and around London, showed great interest in my own experience with poisons. I recounted how once I had found one of my father's cows killed and partly eaten by a wild beast. Later that evening, while I was watching with great caution, I saw two lions slowly approach the carcass. I then took my bow and shot off several poisoned arrows. One of the lions dropped dead, killed on the spot, but the other, badly wounded, roared and ran away. That lion was found dead the next morning, some 300 yards away.

The poison, made from the juice of a tree, has such a quality that if an animal is shot in this way, its flesh may be eaten without ill effect, providing the animal which is rendered senseless has its throat cut, as our law dictates. I explained that should any of my people be struck by such a poisoned arrow, they could be saved by the application of such a herb as an antidote.

Maurice Johnson, who I have mentioned, was a most interesting character, and quite different from Dr Mortimer. He had been born in the late 1680s in Spalding, a quiet country town in the county of Lincolnshire, and had become a Barrister at Law. But it was for his interest in and collection of antiquities that he had become best known. Indeed, many of his friends and colleagues referred to him affectionately as The Antiquary. Always keen to broaden his knowledge and widen his circle of enquiring minds, Mr Johnson founded the Spalding Gentlemen's Society in 1710.

This learned society had humble beginnings, initially convening meetings in a Spalding coffeehouse where friends met to discuss antiques and read the then newly published Tatler periodical. The journal would soon assume significant importance among leading thinkers of the time. The aim of the Society was to support 'mutual benevolence' and the improvement in 'the liberal sciences and in polite learning'. What a noble aspiration! Among its members were great men like the scientist Sir Isaac Newton; the poet Alexander Pope and the Scottish nobleman, Francis Scott, the 2nd Duke of Buccleuch, a man of great learning who, in 1732, was the first to be honoured as the Society's patron.

Although my English was far from acceptable, I could understand enough, as well as make myself understood to engage in the discourses that illuminated the minds of all the gentlemen, as well as several impressive ladies, who frequented the social gatherings to which I was invited. While the finely attired men seemed intent on making an impression with a demonstration of their wit and intelligence, these ladies of privileged families seemed more content to entertain – to make polite conversation and, above all else, to look and smell attractive in their fine dresses of many-layered fabrics.

Often my eyes would be met by flirtatious glances from these attractive ladies, even to the extent of making me feel uncomfortable with my unseemly thoughts and urges. In my home I was used to seeing women in their natural state, but here they seemed to be more alluring for their concealment, with perhaps just a portion of their breasts – hereabouts described as 'bosoms' or 'rising moons' – displayed as a hint of their womanhood.

I could not have been more contented. I learnt much about the lives of this most fortunate stratum of English society. For the most part, these people of breeding and education demonstrated a strong religious foundation – including tolerance of and curiosity in my own beliefs. While they may have been far removed from the poverty and hardship of the general population, of which the evidence was all about us, they expressed considerable compassion and demonstrated a philanthropic will to assist the downtrodden whenever possible.

It must be said that they themselves lived well, wining and dining liberally – and to my eyes, to excess – while enjoying some of the pleasurable activities that only money could provide. Several of our number enjoyed hunting and fishing, which amused me somewhat, given that their main preoccupation seemed to be more the desire for sport rather than for the quest for food or safety as in my country. But they listened courteously, and with some interest, to my stories of legitimate fishing and hunting expeditions.

I explained that for my countrymen, hunting elephant for their ivory tusks was an important occupation, essential for trading activities. Elephants can be fearsome beasts, made even more so by their size, and they hold a great hatred for those other frightening animals, the lions. I myself have seen an elephant thrust a lion's head into the mud and hold it there until it was smothered. I have also been told that an elephant once seized a lion and imprisoned the beast's head in a fork in a tree.

These stories may have informed and amused my educated gentlemen friends, but their telling only served to remind me of my homeland, my traditional way of life which seemed, from this distance, to be so much purer, more natural than the one I was experiencing here in England. I still hankered to return home; to be truly free once more.

Fortunately, my growing circle of friends seemed to understand my feelings and they showed every sign of wanting to assist me. This was borne out by a letter penned in London by Joseph Ames in November 1733. The recipient was William Bogdani, Clerk of the Ordnance of the Tower of London who happened to be the brother-in-law of Maurice Johnson. I was not surprised to learn that Mr Bogdani was himself a prolific letter writer and a prominent member of the Spalding Gentlemen's Society. So enamoured was he with the society and its genteel provincial setting that he once described Spalding in a letter as a town 'separated from the rest of mankind'.

But I digress. The letter Mr Ames sent to Mr Bogdani speaks for itself, so I set it down here in its entirety:

London 17 Novr 1733

Good Sr

In obedience to your Request as well as my own Inclination, to make known the Character of a Virtuous Stranger: I shall give it to you, as I have received it both from himself & Others – know then Sr that Job the son of Abraham, the Son of Solyman,

*the Son of Abdula &c was born to Abraham by his
wife Tautamata About 31 Years agoe: his Father being
a Mahometan Prist; and of Note in the Languages was
chose to be Tutor to the present Governour Samba the
son of Galaga, when his brother Boub governed Foutrè
in Affrica; at a Town called Bondo situate on a Branch
of the River Niger or Sanaga about the Latitude 13 and
Longtitude 8 from London Job was born. His youth
was taken up in Learning, so that he could repeat the
Koran by memory at 15 Years of Age He hath Learned
Three Languages Besides the Fuller which is his Mother
Tongue: vizt the Arabic, the Ganna & the Gallumbo
& since the English. In his more advanced Years he
taught Youth Arabic & dealt for Negroes &c, & in one
Journey went five Weeks from home towards Egypt.
He says that the Arabians come into his Country for
a certain Root, by which they cause Poisons (Perhaps
it might be of Use to Us to know It.) That he hath 2
Wives, 4 Children, 18 Servants, 3 Houses, 73 Head of
Black Cattle, besides Asses and other Things: That his
time was spent in the Offices of the Priesthood and
taking care of his Plantation.*

*He went at the desire of his Father to sell two
Negro Boys with a Caution not to go beyond the
River Gambia but not meeting with the Success he
desired ventured further with the Cattle, a People
called Mandingoes watch'd an Opportunity and seiz'd
Him; and sold Him & his Servant to one Capt.: Pike
in the service of Mr Henry Hunt Merchant in London,
to whome before he had offered his Boys; so that the
Capt. remembring him, gave him leave to write for his
Ransom Monday Tuesday Wednesday & Thursday
in March 1731. But the time being too short, He was*

obliged to sail of Fryday & carrying Job to Maryland, and there delivered Him to Mr Vachell Denton (Factor to Mr Hunt) who sold him to Mr Alexander Tulcey of Kent Island in Chesapeach Bay a little to the East of Annapolis, who soon employed Him to keep his Cattle, where he wrote that Arabick Letter that was after sent over in Mr Hunt's Packet (which I took a copy of and endeavoured to get it translated).

He spent much time with Mr John Humphrys Minister of Annapolis to teach Him Arabick. It hapened that Mr Oglethorpe whether out of Tenderness, or thinking he might be usefull, desired Mr Hunt to purchase Him & left Bond to be satisfied by the Honourable the Affrican Company: accordingly He was brought over in May last, & lodged at Lime-house, where he hath wrote all the Koran over twice. He speaks tolerable English, & waits expecting to be sent to Gambia by the first Ship that goes in the Companys Service. I might have enlarged but let this Suffice at present from

Your affectionate Friend J Ames

Readers will be familiar with much of this narrative, as it was I who, as best I could, had provided Mr Ames with an account of my life and the tragic circumstances that had brought me to England. But I was heartened with his compliments, especially mention of me being a 'Virtuous Stranger' and the sympathetic way he set down my natural desire to return to Gambia.

Fortunately, by this time there was a growing consensus among my acquaintances that my future needed to be made more secure and that I should be freed from the bond still held by Capt. Hunt in accordance with Mr Oglethorpe's wishes.

As I was to learn, several of my influential acquaintances had generously contributed to a fund to purchase my freedom. In the end, it was the Royal African Company that had remained at the centre of activities to keep me secure, comfortable and provisioned with funds; that was instrumental in finding a way to release me from bondage.

Richard Spence, the company's secretary, asked Capt. Hunt to attend a meeting in African House – the company's headquarters in Leadenhall Street – on the morning of Thursday, November 15 at which he was requested to deliver Mr Oglethorpe's bond. Capt. Hunt was also asked to bring me, 'the Black whom you brought from Carolina'.

Negotiations ensued, and it was agreed that the company would pay £59. 6s. 11 ½d to cover the cost of Mr Oglethorpe's bond, the interest on the principal from May 3 and some thirteen pounds, three shillings to cover my accommodation, food, clothing and other costs incurred on my behalf by Capt. Hunt.

At the time, I was still residing in Cheshunt with Mr Bluett and on November 20 I learnt of these latest developments in a letter brought by a footman in the employ of Samuel Holden – a wealthy merchant involved in the African trade to whom I had also been introduced. Like Mr Bluett, Mr Holden was a tenant of the Duke of Portland, living in one of the handsome residences on the Theobalds Estate owned by the 2nd Duke of Montagu. I was informed that the bond had been paid to Capt. Hunt and I should immediately pack my belongings for a journey back to London. I was being moved to the company's headquarters, African House in Leadenhall Street, where the caretaker James Forbes would look after me.

My few months in Cheshunt, mainly with Mr Bluett, had been mostly a happy and fruitful period, despite anxiety about my ownership and a persistent longing to be back in Africa with my family. The bond between Mr Bluett and I became stronger with each passing day, although it also became apparent, as my understanding improved, that he might be drawing some unrealistically worthy impression of my character. In his published memoir of my life, which he began preparing at this time, he recorded:

> *'In his natural Temper there appeared a happy Mixture of the Grave and the Cheerful, a gentle Mildness, guarded by a proper Warmth, and a kind and compassionate Disposition towards all that were in Distress.'*

He must have been seeing me as a saint! I therefore felt obliged to correct the impression by pointing out that I could be uncompromising and courageous if the need arises. To provide some proof, I recounted the story of my fight with fifteen wild bandits during which I was run through the leg with a spear.

During my time in Cheshunt I was fortunate to be introduced to the gentry and noted intellectuals in the area and further afield. I gradually became accustomed to their way of life: their large, comfortable houses; their fine clothes; the refined and genteel way in which they conducted themselves when assembled together; and the array of shiny tableware – glasses, cutlery, and expensive ceramic cups, plates and dishes – with which they consumed their rich array of food and drink. All this was so sharply in contrast to my way of life back home. It brought confusion to my eyes and demeanour. But, thanks to patient guidance on the part of my hosts, it was not too long before I was feeling at least reasonably comfortable within this society.

As I hope I have shown, among the most prominent of the fine gentlemen who had welcomed and assisted me were Mr

Ames and Sir Hans Sloane. On arrival in African House I met Mr Ames and expressed my thanks for all the many favours afforded me and gave my assurance that I would make all the returns I could. Mr Ames kindly wrote to Sir Hans, passing on my words of appreciation.

It soon became apparent that plans for my repatriation back to Africa were moving at great pace. I learnt that the Royal African Company was fitting out a ship to sail for the Gambia that might leave in about a month's time – around Christmastime, according to my Christian friends. It was intimated that I might well be on that ship. Allah be praised. And steps were being taken to secure my freedom from the ownership now held by the company. Several influential men, including Samuel Holden and Nathaniel Brassey, a banker in London's Lombard Street, started a charitable subscription to repay the company and set me free.

My friend, Mr Bluett, wrote to Sir Hans Sloane on December 3, explaining that a ship of a Mr Hyde would be leaving very soon for my country and that a subscription had been started to redeem my freedom. The money was 'paid into the hands of Mr Richard Harding at Hamlin's Coffee House, Swithin's Alley, near the Exchequer,' wrote Mr Bluett, adding, 'The Subscription began on Friday night and seems to promise fair.'

But it soon transpired that Sir Hans, and some of his followers, were deeply concerned by this turn of events. Sir Hans felt that my future was more assured under the existing arrangement. He was confident that the company would behave honourably and would do what was best in my interest. Furthermore, he argued, nothing should be done without James Oglethorpe's consent.

So, Sir Hans asked that I should go with Mr Ames and meet with Mr Bluett at Hamlin's Coffee House, a popular meeting place for refreshment and discourse. But it was not a happy meeting. My companions strongly disagreed with each other. Mr Ames argued that I was now in good hands and I should remain content with my present situation. Mr Ames addressed Mr Bluett directly with pointed questions: 'What would happen if the company refused to part with Job? Have you asked them that question?'

And then...

'What would Mr Oglethorpe say about your proposals, Mr Bluett?'

When questioned about how much money had been subscribed to the charitable fund, Mr Bluett replied that so far twenty-eight pounds – or perhaps it was twenty-eight guineas – had been collected. Mr Ames expressed a desire that subscribers should make use of the money to my benefit. On that friendlier note, we all departed, although I could tell that Mr Bluett was still troubled and in a melancholy mood.

But then neither of us could know that there would soon be developments affecting both my freedom and repatriation. In the meantime, my passage into English high society – a journey that was providing me with a privileged insight into the minds and customs of the rich and powerful – was about to provide me with even greater surprises.

CHAPTER 6

Feted by royalty; painted
by a top portraitist

◇◇◇

The Envoys of the Bey of Tunis were charming and colourful gentlemen. Around this time – in the autumn of 1733 – they were in London on a goodwill visit to the court of King George II and Queen Caroline of Ansbach on behalf of the Ruler of Tunis, Ali II ibn Hussein. They had brought with them five magnificent Arab horses as a gift for King George. This was a most appropriate present as the King, an ardent huntsman, had a great love of horses. He maintained a breeding stud at Hampton Court with Richard Lumley, 2nd Earl of Scarborough, as his Master of Horse.

Sadly, as I learnt (there was a report in *The London Magazine*) on October 11, one of the Envoys attended the Hampton Court audience with their Majesties while in mourning. He had lost his father, mother, wife and five children to the dreaded plague since his arrival in England. It is hard to imagine the grief of that good man, dutifully fulfilling his role as an emissary far from home while bearing the pain of having his closest family so cruelly taken from him. Although, at that time we had not met, news of this personal tragedy affected me greatly. I shared that man's grief and took comfort from reading appropriate passages from the Holy Koran. To Allah we belong and to Allah we return.

It was suggested by some of my associates that I might like to meet the Envoys given our shared religion and African connections, and an audience was duly arranged for a day in early December. I must admit to some apprehension as I was formally introduced, because I had scant knowledge of the correct protocol in such circumstances. However, I need not have worried. I was received very civilly and quickly put at my ease.

In many ways, our conversation flowed more freely than I had experienced with my more-established acquaintances in England, for it helped that we all had a knowledge of Arabic and some basic English. What is more, we found ourselves sharing a common culture and view of life, rooted in our Islamic faith. We talked much about how my Fula people in West Africa could trace their heritage back to North Africa – who knows, perhaps in the kingdom now known as Tunis – many centuries ago. Prompted by my questions, my hosts described the honour and courtesy shown to them by their Majesties in the magnificent surroundings of Hampton Court. But it was not long before attention turned on me.

The Envoys expressed great interest in my life, in my time before my capture, my experiences as a slave and prisoner in America, and my apparent freedom and entry into society here in England. Our conversations seemed to last much longer than perhaps were originally intended, for I was invited to stay on and take a hearty dinner with my hosts.

By now, feeling quite at ease with fellow African Muslims, I was in full flood. I emphasised the many kindnesses shown to me by my acquaintances, several of whom were notable gentlemen whose reputations were known to the Envoys. I expressed how grateful I was for the hospitality shown to me, especially given my humble upbringing in a faraway place and my shameful predicament as a slave in Maryland. Emboldened, I also told the Envoys how anxious I was to be freed from my bondage as a slave – however comfortable my present state might be – and how eager I was to return to Africa.

'I do miss my family and friends so much', I said, adding, 'I just long to be back in familiar surroundings, to return to my traditional way of life.'

My hosts expressed their understanding and sympathy for my predicament and presented me with a guinea as a contribution towards a fund for my return journey.

'Perhaps this will help in a small way,' said one of my hosts.

Today I smile at the thought of that generous gift and its significance to my circumstances at that time. For the 'guinea' became the popular name for the coinage because most of the gold used in its early minting came from Guinea in West Africa. Some of the coins even depicted an elephant to symbolise the gold trading activities of the Royal African Company.

The emissaries kindly invited me to call on them again the Friday following our meeting but, in the event, I was unable to attend as I was so busy preparing myself for an early departure for Africa. I was so fortunate to have been given so many gifts, including a timekeeping watch with which I was exceedingly pleased, and all of which needed to be packed carefully for the voyage.

I admit these preparations were being made in a maelstrom of emotion. I was excited because I had learnt that the fitting out of a ship that might carry me was in a well-advanced stage. And yet I was deeply concerned, because my freedom was still unsettled and I was not certain that I would be able to leave. I knew that Sir Hans and Mr Ames continued to oppose the scheme to purchase my freedom from the Royal African Company, a situation that filled me with great anxiety.

It is with some shame that I now admit that for a time I spurned Mr Ames's attempts to meet with me, given my unhappiness with his stance. I now know this was an immature attitude to adopt – one that would certainly have earned a rebuke from my father – given all the kindness shown to me by Mr Ames.

In the event, it mattered not, for at this time – Thursday, December 20, to be precise – Mr Holden and Mr Brassey were meeting with Sir Bibye Lake at the African Coffee House in Leadenhall Street to discuss the proposals for my release from bondage. Other subscriptions to my freedom fund had been made – including a two-guinea subscription from none other than Admiral Sir Charles Wager, the First Lord of the Admiralty – and the requisite funds were close to being met.

Thankfully, Sir Bibye accepted that the proposals were reasonable and agreed to recommend their acceptance to other officers in the company. A week later, at a meeting of the Court of Assistance, it was ordered:

'That a Certificate be prepared Setting forth That Simon otherwise called Job the Gambia Black lately brought from Maryland, is acquitted and discharged from all Claims or demands that this Company have or can have against him on any account and further declaring him to be a Freeman; and That he is at liberty to take his passage to Africa in any of the Company's Ships, or in

any other Ship or Ships that he shall choose in order to
return to his Native Country, and That the Company's
seal be affixed there to and the same be thereupon
delivered to the said Simon otherwise called Job.'

The certificate itself, defining in lofty English an act of manumission, was a handsome document, set out in large letters and authenticated with a large company seal. I was thrilled to receive it, for it set down the terms of my freedom in the most unambiguous manner (although I admit, at the time it challenged my complete comprehension, given my still basic understanding of the English language). It states:

'Know all Men by these Present, That we the Royal
African Company of England have acquitted and do
by these Present acquit and for ever discharge Simon,
otherwise called Job a black lately brought over from
Maryland of and from all Manner of Claims and
Demands of us against him on any Account whatsoever,
And we do further hereby for us and our Successors
declare that from and after this day the said Simon
otherwise called Job is a free Man and is at Liberty to
take his Passage to Africa in any of our Ships or in any
other Ship or Ships which he shall chuse, in order to
return to his Native Country. In Witness whereof we
have caused our Common Seal to be hereunto Affixed
this 27th Day of December in the Year of our Lord 1733.
　　'By order of the Court of Assistants of the Royal
African Company of England.
　　'Richd. Spence.'

Even now I find it difficult to express the relief and happiness I felt when I first received this document and, with the help of

Mr Bluett, studied each word and its meaning. Indeed, I find my eyes misting up even now as I recall those feelings. And yet I cannot cast out of my mind those miserable, persecuted slaves with whom I endured the passage to Maryland and with whom I laboured in the fields of Annapolis. It is impossible to conceive that such freedom was conferred on them.

And with closer examination, and in my impassioned state, I could not help but find as abhorrent the words and sentiment expressed in that very certificate. It raised some fundamental issues with which I have grappled even into my old age.

What right has one man to own another, to be in a lofty position to 'acquit' and 'discharge' a slave from bondage? Who can assume the privilege of granting liberty to another man to take passage in a ship? Why should any man be labelled with an unwanted name – Simon, in my case – or an unjustified description? I will always resent being labelled 'a black'. I cannot believe that the God of Muslims and Christians would sanction such a document being drawn up in His name.

And yet I have to accept my own willing part in this business called slavery. Why is it that I did not have these feelings during my days of trading captives? And would I feel the same when I returned to Africa?

Even in this maelstrom of conflicting feelings I felt grateful to the eminent persons, the friends and acquaintances, who campaigned for my release from the powerful Royal African Company. The issue of my bondage was finally settled on Thursday, January 10, 1734, when Nathaniel Brassey generously agreed to donate twenty pounds being the balance of donations still outstanding. He was thus able to hand over the full amount of £59. 6s. 11d. being the sum paid by the company to Capt. Hunt. Mr Brassey, who had followed his father into banking, was also a Member of Parliament. I found him a most interesting man, partly because he had grown up in a Quaker household, following customs and practises that set them apart from other religions and sects of their time. I was told Quakers were seen by many as peculiar people but to me they had the appealing distinction of regarding everyone as equal in the sight of their God.

Until the memorable meeting with the emissaries of the Bey of Tunis my conversations with privileged members of English society had largely been confined to such men – and their ladies – associated with trade, banking, and science. But my social circle was soon to be extended onto an even higher plane.

I was still residing contentedly at African House, ably looked after by James Forbes, at some cost to the company. I was allowed eight shillings and six pence for my board and lodging, and a further nine pence for my laundry and mending. And then there was the cost to the company of transporting my goods from one place to another: eighteen shillings and six pence in just the fourteen weeks between March 20 and June 27.

Every effort was being made to make me feel relaxed in this strange new world. The hospitality was really appreciated, for I was now feeling much more confident about moving freely among my friends and meeting them in their homes. It was at one of these meetings with Sir Hans, who remained a supportive friend despite our disagreements over my bondage, that I mentioned I would dearly like to meet the royal family, of whom the Envoys had spoken so warmly. I knew this was wishing for a great deal. After all, why would any royal person want to meet me? I had nothing to offer.

But Sir Hans, as physician to King George II (and his father before him) and one of his distinguished friends, His Grace, the 2nd Duke of Montagu, clearly used their influence and they did manage to secure an audience with their Majesties –

both the King and his Queen Caroline. What an honour!

Sir Hans had insisted that I could not meet the royal family unless I was properly dressed. Apparently, the King was very particular about such matters as etiquette and dress code. It was felt that my European apparel would not be appropriate or suitable, even though I had been given a smart suit, specially made for me – 'Ajouba or Job a negro' – in a drugget woolen fabric. The records show that this suit cost the Royal African Company no less than two pounds and ten shillings. Even so, we agreed that it would be more appropriate for me to wear traditional, African clothing. But I had none with me.

Fortunately, Nathaniel Brassey was on hand again, this time to pay for a fine white thawb of rich cotton to be made for me under my own instruction. When I first tried on this traditional ankle-length garment and examined myself in the mirror, I beamed with happiness. I stood tall, drawing myself to my full height of around five feet ten inches. I looked noble. And I looked African. I am sure my father would have been so proud of me.

It was a chilly winter's day, still early in 1734, that I was taken by carriage to Kensington Palace, accompanied by the Duke and Sir Hans.[20] My first impression was of the great royal garden laid out in deceptive simplicity, with sweeping lawns, trees and shrubs, to provide a quiet oasis in this noisy, frantic city. Apparently, members of the public were permitted to stroll through these gardens, although none was visible on the day I was there, because the King and Queen were present in the palace.

Courtiers met us at the great entrance of the palace. We were shown up a marble staircase and taken into a state room, called the Presence Chamber, to await the royal couple. The room was not as large as I had expected, given the grandness of the palace building. But my eyes were dazzled. It was hard to focus, given the richness and splendour of this room. The walls were filled with paintings in gold frames. Even the ceiling was decorated in the most elaborate fashion. The fireplace was a feature of the room.

Sir Hans explained this palace was a favourite with the royal couple, the centre of court life, especially during the colder months of the year, where the great and the good, including politicians and intellectuals, vied for the King's favours. In a short while a courtier announced the entry of the King and Queen and, as was the custom, we all bowed solemnly as we were approached.

King George II was not the tallest of men, although he carried himself in an erect and somewhat stiff fashion. I supposed this was how royalty walked. His facial features were striking with his broad, high forehead; his long nose and protruding blue eyes. But it was his expressive mouth which seemed to betray his innermost feelings. There was the merest hint of a smile which suggested a genuine welcome and a quizzical expression that betrayed a fascination with what type of man was standing before him. Fortunately, there was no hint of his quick temper that according to gossip among the more privileged and informed of his subjects, seemed to be a hallmark of his character.

I knew that the King took a keen interest in foreign affairs and was fluent in many languages although, sadly, not Arabic. I was therefore pleased and honoured that he showed a real interest in my upbringing near the Gambia and he seemed genuinely sympathetic with my desire – now as a freed man – to return home as quickly as possible. He even indicated that he hoped that, following my welcome and the hospitality I had received in England, I would be prepared to maintain links and help with trading activities between our two countries.[21]

I had been advised to answer when questioned but wait

to be spoken to. It soon became apparent that the King was not as accustomed to casual conversation as some that I had met. In contrast, Queen Caroline soon put me at my ease as we engaged in a warmer and more natural dialogue. She, too, was unusually striking (maybe it is a certain aura that surrounds royal persons) although I would describe her as being pleasant and comely rather than truly beautiful. However, what was evident from her reputation and from our discussion, was that Her Majesty had a lively and inquisitive mind, one she used to wield undoubted influence from behind the throne. Clearly, Queen Caroline was not to be underestimated.

Her opening remarks to me concerned my gown with which she was clearly impressed. But her observations and comments quickly turned to more fundamental matters – my religious beliefs and practises, and practical aspects of living in West Africa. It was the Queen who mentioned the King's passion for hunting, enquiring how we gathered food for our families. We also discussed health issues, which did not come as a surprise, for I knew from my conservations with Sir Hans that the Queen took a keen interest in science and medicine and was well-versed in the activities and the opinions of leading scientists of the Royal Society.

It was in more general matters relating to the wider world that Her Majesty demonstrated most interest, as well as considerable knowledge. It was only in the previous summer, in this room, that the King and Queen had granted an audience with a delegation from the Creek Tribe of indigenous Americans from the Yamacraw nation, whose lands had been appropriated into the British colony of Georgia. What a coincidence, for the man who had arranged and accompanied the Yamacraw delegation during their visit to London was none other than James Oglethorpe, the Governor of Georgia, who had been so instrumental in securing my own freedom from captivity in Maryland.

All too soon our audience was ending, but not before Queen Caroline performed a most unexpected ceremony. A courtier subtly handed Her Serene Highness a small package, which she in turn presented to me with her good wishes and a wonderful smile. It was a most handsome gold watch, the most treasured of the many gifts that had been bestowed on me since my unorthodox arrival in England.

As our carriage took us away from Kensington Palace, I reflected on what had been for me a surreal experience, far removed from my once-humble life in my unadorned but still beautiful homeland in Africa. And yet my day of privilege, of consorting with leading aristocratic figures of the age, was not yet over. For that evening, His Grace the Duke of Montagu had invited me to dine with him and others of nobility at his London home, Montagu House, on the banks of the River Thames in Whitehall.[22]

Impressed as I was with the size and opulence of this waterside mansion in the heart of the city, I was told it was quite modest when compared with the Duke's previous London residence, vacated only a couple of years earlier. This home, situated in Bloomsbury, was described as the grandest private residence in London. It was on the scale and grandeur of a royal palace, influenced in style and content by the most sophisticated French taste. (The remembrance of this revelation brought a smile to my face in later years when it became apparent that in trading and political matters the French and English could be the bitterest of enemies.)

It was plain that the Duke was a man of immense wealth and influence. And there were few in London who could claim a more distinguished career. His Grace had the distinction of being a Knight of the Garter and member of the Order of the

Bath – two of the highest honours in the land. He had also been admitted as a fellow of the Royal Society and a fellow of the Royal College of Physicians. The King's father – George I – had appointed the Duke as High Constable at his Coronation while at the Coronation of George II he had been given the privilege of carrying the sceptre and cross.

I was fascinated to learn that King George I had also granted him the islands of St Lucia and St Vincent, along with the titles of Governor and Captain-General. His Grace had hoped to enjoy the same rights and financial benefits in the Caribbean as he had enjoyed on his coastal estate at Beaulieu in Hampshire. But by all accounts this proved to be a short-lived, ill-fated enterprise.

The Duke himself never sailed to the islands but appointed a merchant sea captain, Nathaniel Uring, as Deputy Governor who, along with new colonists, was expelled from the islands by the French, who regarded the land as neutral territory. The Duke is said to have lost a great deal of money – over £40,000[23] – because of this failed undertaking. That setback, which would have ruined many a rich man, did not seem to have had much impact on His Grace's reputation, optimism or pocket, for it was plain for me to see he remained highly influential (there were several other members of nobility present at the dinner) and very, very rich.

And yet I was struck mostly by his generous hospitality, kindness and keen interest in others around him. He had a compelling reputation for his humour and love of practical jokes, but he was also a scholar, with a great interest in the advancement of scientific knowledge. I was quickly put at ease, especially by the genuine interest he displayed in my background and my way of life back home in Africa. In return, he was happy to share his knowledge of modern appliances and practises that marked the path of progress in this modern world; a way of life that I could never have envisaged back in my simple township.

Our worlds and our way of life may have been so very different and yet at no time was I made to feel inferior or patronised. He showed a strong humanitarian spirit and demonstrated respect for his fellow man, whatever his colour or background.

Many years after our encounter I learnt of stories that showed how he had befriended and encouraged others – among them a young black Jamaican, Francis Williams, the youngest son of freed black slaves; and Ignatius Sancho, the orphaned son of a black slave who was born on an Atlantic slave ship and was cared for by three sisters living in Greenwich. One day the Duke met the boy by chance. Like me he invited Sancho to one of his homes, lent him books and encouraged his education and advancement.[24]

I think it was this kindness and spirit of openness that led His Grace to become a mentor and patron throughout my remaining time in England. On several occasions, he took me by carriage on excursions into the country, to Ditton Park, twenty miles to the west of London and close to a village called Datchet. Here His Grace had a grand house, surrounded by a moat, gardens and farmland.[25]

There was so much to be admired in the house which had been a royal hunting lodge in the time of Queen Elizabeth. What struck me most about the house was its imposing tower with its battlements. But what impressed me even more were the everyday tools and gadgets that his servants used and were encouraged to demonstrate.

I was fascinated to see how these implements could ease the physical workload of those toiling in the fields, gardens or house. And I was overwhelmed when His Grace made a gift to me of many of the instruments, implements and tools that had clearly captured my interest. He explained that they might be put to good use when I returned home to Africa. What kindness!

Several other of the Duke's influential friends and associates, some of whom were present at our first dinner, also presented me with similarly useful gifts, which His Grace kindly arranged to be packed in sturdy chests in readiness for the voyage back to my homeland. I am embarrassed to record that the names of some of these notables have slipped my memory, but I do recall the noble 9th Earl of Pembroke and the young Prince William were especially generous.

Henry, the Earl of Pembroke, who had strong royal connections, had acceded to the title in only the previous year, in 1733, following the death of his father. Yet he had already become established as a courtier and close associate of the King. At the time of our meeting he was Colonel of the King's Own Regiment of Horse, a position previously held by the Duke of Montagu. The Earl looked every inch a nobleman; then in his early forties, he was powerfully built with strong features and clearly benefited from regular sporting exercise.

Prince William, on the other hand, was barely thirteen years old when we met, although even then he had the assured manner and confidence of a mature young man. In this respect he reminded me somewhat of myself and my friends at that age for, by tradition, we were also encouraged to assume manly duties at an early age. The Prince was the youngest son of King George II, and from the age of five he had bestowed on him an array of prestigious titles, including that of the Duke of Cumberland. He was also a Knight of the Garter and a Knight of the Bath. No wonder he had such noble airs. I felt extremely privileged that he took such an interest in me.

The confidence that was so evident at our meeting would be displayed many times during the Prince's later military career. A Major General at the age of twenty-one, he went on to accomplish some notable military achievements, including the defeat of the Jacobites at the Battle of Culloden in 1746.

Just like the many battles back in my homeland, the Scottish Jacobites had been engaged in a war of royal succession, aimed at returning the House of Stuart, the descendants of King James II, to the throne of Great Britain. George Frideric Handel, the great composer who was prominent and often talked about in London during my time there, composed the oratorio *Judas Maccabaeus* with the chorus 'See the conquering hero comes' as a tribute to this great victory.

But the Prince's reputation was also tarnished for the way he had led his troops against the Jacobites, conducting massacres and atrocities not only at Culloden but also throughout the Highlands of Scotland. For these acts he gained another title, bestowed by Scottish Highlanders as well as those wider afield, including in England. He was called 'Butcher Cumberland'.

I was touched, but somewhat embarrassed, with the generosity of my new-found friends. I had received so many gifts, yet I had little opportunity to return their kindness. Of course, I had with me no gifts or mementos of Africa with which to reciprocate.

However, during my time in England I had spent much time in a careful but pleasurable fashion to write the Koran from memory. I had managed to produce three copies, much to the surprise of many of my acquaintances. One of these I presented to His Grace, the Duke of Montagu who, despite his lofty station, had been so kind to me in so many ways. Another I gave to Nathaniel Brassey, who had been so instrumental in raising funds for my release and, I hoped, my return to Africa, as well as paying for my gown to attend Court. The third copy I presented to Joseph Smith, the grocer who, during my weekly visits to his home, had demonstrated so much kindness and empathy for my situation.[26]

But these were gifts for just three of the many who had befriended and helped me since my arrival in Limehouse. How could I thank all the others in a tangible way? The answer to that riddle came when I was persuaded to sit for a portrait that I could leave in England. I must admit I was somewhat uneasy with this prospect. My Muslim beliefs made me wary of making images of humans who might be viewed in an idolatrous way. Eventually I was persuaded by Mr Bluett and others that the portrait would be used only for casual viewing, as a reminder of my stay, rather than as a focus for any kind of worship.

'I assure you, we would never worship any such picture,' Mr Bluett told me.

I accepted his assurance, for I had seen during my visits to palaces and country houses that rich men and women enjoy displaying fine portraits of their ancestors and associates. I too had been impressed with the skill of artists who could generate such accurate depictions of human figures through the application of paints.

My friends had chosen an aspiring young artist, William Hoare,[27] from Suffolk to paint my picture. Still in his late twenties, some six years younger than me, Mr Hoare had been spending much of his time in Italy, studying and copying masterpieces, but his skill as a portraitist was already beginning to be recognised in England.

We had several sittings, during which Mr Hoare not only captured my likeness, an achievement in itself, but also a depiction of my inner self. I felt relaxed and at peace in his presence. I remember that the artist first concentrated on painting my face, which was hardly surprising given this was to be a portrait. But then he asked how I wished to be dressed in the painting. At the time, I was wearing everyday English clothing provided by my benefactors.

'I think it is right that I should be seen wearing my native African dress,' I said.

Mr Hoare looked concerned and ill at ease.

'But I cannot draw this dress without seeing it,' he explained.

This made me ponder and reflect on the many religious paintings I had seen during my travels in England. I still remember my response, that seemed to come to my mind in a flash.

'If you cannot draw a dress you never saw, why do some of you painters presume to draw God, whom no-one has ever seen?' I asked. Mr Hoare smiled. That was his only reply.

It was agreed that I should be painted wearing the white cotton gown that I had worn for my audience with their Majesties, along with a white and crimson turban, and one of my copies of the Koran strung from my neck.[28] And this is how I was portrayed. While I was nervous about being depicted in such a way, I must say I was both pleased and impressed with the finished portrait that I hoped would serve as a fitting reminder of my extraordinary visit to England.

Around the time that my portrait was being painted I found that my London society friends were planning to bestow on me yet another honour. Throughout much of 1733 and the early part of 1734, I had become increasingly aware of the activities of a learned society that, since its inception in 1710, had attracted some of the leading thinkers in British Society.

Surprisingly this prestigious organisation was not based in London but in Spalding, a small market town in the Lincolnshire Fens. This is the very same Spalding Gentlemen's Society that I have mentioned previously, founded by a local barrister, Maurice Johnson, who had featured so prominently in my campaign for freedom and repatriation.

The organisation was established with the most noble of ideals: as a '*Society of Gentlemen, for the supporting of mutual benevolence, and their improvement in the liberal sciences and in polite learning*'. And now I learnt that I was being proposed as a member. Apart from Mr Johnson, the principal movers behind this honour were Joseph Ames and William Bogdani. This trio had much in common, for Mr Bogdani was not only a friend of Mr Ames, but his wife Penelope was also a relation of Mr Johnson.

The formal application took place at a meeting of society members held in the Office of Ordnance in the historic Tower of London on Thursday, May 23, 1734. It seemed much of the London activity of the society took place in or around the Tower of London.

First, an account of my life was read by Mr Johnson in his capacity as secretary. I am both embarrassed and humbled when I read the words set down as a lengthy letter written in London by Mr Ames to Mr Bogdani on November 17 the previous year. That letter, you might remember, gives an account of my life, education and character; the one in which I was described as a 'Virtuous Stranger'.

The proposal stated that I, as a 'Mahometan Preist of learning from Bondo', should be admitted as an honorary member of the society. My application, which had been written for me, was then tabled:

'*Being informed that there is a Society of Men of learning in Spalding in Lincolnshire known by the Name of the Gentlemen's Society of Spalding am very desireous of the honour of being admitted a Member thereof, being made acquainted with and approveing of their Institution for the publick Good.*'

My membership was formally proposed by two of the society's members: James West of Lincoln's Inn, a Fellow of the Royal Society and a noted antiquary with a deep interest in politics; and George Holmes, Deputy Keeper of the Records in the Tower of London. Like Mr West, George Holmes was a Fellow of the Royal Society with a deep knowledge of antiquities. The minutes of the Spalding society show that with the assent of Mr Bogdani and Mr Johnson I was 'accordingly proposed being a learned and worthy person'.

The proposal was considered at a meeting of seven members on Thursday, June 6, 1734, with Mr John Jackson in the chair. Mr Jackson was a Spalding merchant and vice president of the society. The organisation's minutes recorded the 'learned & worthy Job Jalla was upon Ballott elected and admitted an Honorary Member of this Society'. The honour bestowed on me was amplified when I learnt that at the same meeting the society agreed to invite the 7th Viscount Falkland, Lucius Charles Carey, to become a member as well. Truly, I was in esteemed company.

Sadly, I was never able to visit the seat of this august learned society. Spalding is a town in the county of Lincolnshire, lying some 100 miles north of London. Given my impending return to my African homeland, there would not have been sufficient time to undertake this English expedition. But I was pleased to show my appreciation for the great honour bestowed on me by writing a note in Arabic script that could be added to the society's minute book. This note, acknowledging the proposal and my application of my membership, was then sent to Spalding in a letter where it was copied into the minute book, in a very fine hand by all accounts, by my dear friend Maurice Johnson.[29]

It was one of the final acts of so many kindnesses that had been bestowed on me by some of the greatest men – and women – during my time in England. I could not help but wonder if I could ever again be content and fulfilled with my familiar rural life back in Bondu.

But I did so very much want to go back home to see again the people and places that I love.

CHAPTER 7

Return to Africa

◇◇◇

My mood was not entirely one of lightness. I had been made aware that trading rights in my homeland were contested by the English and French, and there was every possibility of confrontation on my journey to the Gambia. Some relief was to be gained in the ship that the Royal African Company had booked for my passage. She was a modern, well-armed vessel: His Majesty's ship *Dolphin*, a twenty-gun square-rigged snow, built at the Deptford naval dockyard on the Thames, east of London, in 1731, and commissioned for the West India service. She measured 106 feet along the gun deck by thirty feet in the beam with a tonnage of 428 burden. So, the ship seemed fine. But it still worried me what might happen if I fell into French hands, especially as I had become so close to the English and its influential members of society.

I had mentioned this concern at a meeting with Sir Hans Sloane in the company of Sir Randal Macdonell, Captain of the Duc de Bourbon's Lifeguards, who was about to return to the French Court. Monsieur le Duc had been Prime Minister in the Court of King Louis XV.[30] Sir Randal promised he would do all he could to arrange protection for me. In a letter to Sir Hans, written in Monsieur le Duc's country estate at Chantilly on May 25, 1734, Sir Randal provided that valuable reassurance.

My concerns had been raised and acted upon in the Court of Louis XV! The letter stated that the French Secretary of State had personally guaranteed that no action would be taken against me by any French ship. Apparently, Sir Randal had first suggested I might be given a French passport as a form of protection, but the Secretary had said this would be needed only if I sailed in a French vessel. As I was sailing in an English ship a French passport would not be necessary as the two nations were at peace. Sir Hans took a copy of the letter for himself and gave me the original to take with me on my voyage.

As the *Dolphin* was being fitted out to sail at the end of June, most of that month was taken up with farewells, leave-taking and preparations for my departure. I was pleased to learn that the Royal African Company, which was still kindly providing me with lodgings, had paid the significant sum of twelve shillings and six pence for clean bedding to be made ready for me on board *Dolphin* from as early as June 6.

My collection of gifts, that had been so kindly donated by the many friends I had made in England, were securely packed in chests. They included many tools and instruments that I knew would be useful to us in our working lives, as well as an assortment of more personal items. One late addition to these gifts was one I truly treasured. It was a copy of the Pentateuch printed in Arabic, a weighty tome covering the first five books of the Old Testament: Genesis, Exodus, Leviticus, Numbers and Deuteronomy.

This gift, made at the request of Cromwell Mortimer, Second Secretary of the Royal Society and Sir Hans Sloane's medical assistant, was donated by the Society for Promoting Christian Knowledge, that had already kindly given me the New Testament and Psalter printed in Arabic. I was not surprised to hear that Henry Newman, Secretary of the Society, had told Mr Mortimer that these works were as much as I would be able to 'understand or make room for' among my baggage.

Mr Newman was right, because thanks to the generosity of so many people in England, I had assembled a considerable assortment of treasured gifts. In truth I was somewhat embarrassed to learn that the value of these gifts was more than 500 pounds, a fortune beyond my comprehension.[31] Once assembled, this array of luggage was then carried down to Gravesend, on the south bank of the Thames estuary, where Dolphin was moored.

The last night in my lodgings in African House, on June 26, was an uncomfortable affair. I had said my prayers in the normal way and settled down in the soft comfort of my familiar English bed. But I could not sleep. The excitement was coursing through my veins as I anticipated my journey back to my family, my friends and the sights, sounds and smells of my uncomplicated homeland. But I was also troubled.

How much would I miss this privileged, luxurious life in London? Could I ever again be satisfied with the basics of rural life; in Bondu in particular, as well as the wider region of Africa containing the rivers Gambia and Senegal?

Where, in the future, would I find the intellectual stimulus that I had come to appreciate among some of the most intelligent and engaging people you could imagine? Where in Bondu would I find even a hint of the beauty and refinement of the palaces, grand houses and manicured estates that I had been privileged to visit during my stay?

And yet my mind, in this state of turmoil and questioning, kept posing many more questions that I failed to answer. Was the life of privilege that I had witnessed and generously invited to share, as fulfilling and worthy as it was made to appear? My new acquaintances in London may have been much more comfortable than the common people – certainly by the standards I had witnessed in England or experienced back in Africa – but were they any happier or fulfilled?

Perhaps prompted by my religious beliefs and teachings, I found myself even questioning whether it was right that the privileged few should accumulate so much wealth and display their opulence in such a brazen way when it was clear that most of the people – those that I had seen but given a scarce chance to meet – had to make the best of their much more basic and more challenging standard of living.

And yet here I was, tossing and turning in my bed, beginning to criticise the very people who had shown me so much kindness and generosity during my stay in London. How could I be so ungrateful! Worse still... I began to wonder if, by recognising the positives of the privileged world I had experienced, I was not doubting, even betraying, the Islamic faith I held so dear.

After a sleepless night I was up early on Thursday, June 27, ready to be taken by boat down to Gravesend where I was to board the vessel. I was accompanied by a small group from the Royal African Company, including its Secretary, Richard Spence, who were anxious to see that I would be made welcome and comfortable on board the vessel. I was on my way home at last!

It was not the most auspicious departure, at least for the ship's master, Capt. Thomas Freeman. Surprisingly, it was found that my name had been omitted from the list of passengers, although the matter was quickly resolved and my accommodation was located, along with my belongings.

After Capt. Freeman had completed his departure formalities, including accounting for all crew and passengers, we started making our way downriver. Soon we were under full sail, making good progress into the estuary of the Thames and then the open waters of the North Sea. I felt we were really heading home when we turned south, passing the eastern shoreline of the county of Kent.

Our progress was interrupted when we hove to and anchored in an area of sheltered water called the Downs roadstead. We were off the port of Deal, a popular anchorage for ships travelling through the Channel. Here Capt. Freeman received a letter from the hands of a Mr Peter Stone. The company letter from African House, dated July 4, 1734, gave instructions to 'make the best of your way' to Cowes, in the Isle of Wight where Capt. Freeman was to await further instructions.

After this short interlude we were off again, soon turning onto a westerly heading into the Channel that separates England and France. We passed the towering cliffs of white chalk that I had admired on my previous passage. This headland, it seemed, stood as an imposing battlement, protecting England from all hostile invaders.

We sailed on, making for the Solent, the strait that separates the southern mainland from the Isle of Wight, before anchoring off Cowes, on the northern shore of the island. Here, as instructed, Capt. Freeman awaited the arrival of a ship's agent in a boat out of Gosport on the other side of the Solent. Gosport, I learnt, was the usual starting point for the company's voyages to West Africa. Eventually, as final preparations for the voyage were being made, the agent arrived to give last minute instructions and hand over letters and other documents.

Later, I was told by Capt. Freeman, when during the voyage we had established a friendly, confiding relationship, that included in the packet of documents were letters from Richard Spence, the company's secretary, complaining about my omission from the passenger list and emphasising the importance the company regarded my comfort and safety.

I was intrigued why so much urgent activity had been expended on transferring a packet of letters in Cowes. Now I knew. At least some of this correspondence brought on board concerned me. One letter, written to Capt. Freeman, gave a hint of the company's concern. It read:

Capt. Thos Freeman African House
At Cowes 5th July 1734

Sir
I wrote you last night by order of the Court to make the best of your way to Cowes, where you would receive the Company's Packet for Gambia which I accordingly now send inclosed herewith directed for Mr Richard Hull, their First Chief Merchant, or for their Chief Merchants for the time being at Gambia. You are to sign a receipt for the said Packet promising to deliver the same accordingly upon your arrival at Gambia, which you are to return me by Mr Elletson, the Company's Agent, of Gosport, which when done you are to make the best of your way for Gambia, and to follow the Company's Orders, and by all Opportunitys to write to the Company. You should have took Notice of Job amongst the rest of your Passengers of whom you sent me a List.

Inclosed is a Letter from the Court recommending Mr Job to the favour of the Company's Chief at Gambia, which you are to deliver into his own hands, but the Court desire you will read it over to him

carefully and make him as sensible of the Contents thereof as you possibly can. If you should be obliged to put into any other port after your departure from Cowes, I shall hope to hear from you but wish you may gett clear of the Channel and have a Speedy vr good Voyage.
Your Most Humble Sert
R.S.

The company's regard for me was reinforced in that very letter that Capt. Freeman had been instructed to read to me. It was a letter I was to deliver to agents on my arrival in the Gambia. Signed by Sir Bibye Lake, the Governor, Charles Hayes, the Deputy Governor, and ten members of the Court of Assistants, the letter was addressed to 'Messrs. Richard Hull, Charles Orfeur and Hugh Hamilton, Chief Merchants at Gambia'. This is its content:

'Gentlemen
'This will be delivered to you by one Job, a free Black, and Son of a Mahometan Priest, he was formerly taken and sold to one of the private Traders and carried to Mary Land, where he was sold for a Slave, but by the Interest and good Offices of Mr Oglethorpe, has been redeemed in order to be sett at Liberty and sent back to his own Country, he has been here in England for some time and appears to be a very Sober and Ingenious Person, and has met with many favours and civilities here from many Persons of great Rank and worth, who have bestowed upon him several Considerable Presents all which he carries along with him, and as we are very desirous that he should be well and kindly used, while he stays with you, and that all due Care

may be taken to send him with his things safe home to his own Country, we do earnestly recommend him to your Care and Protection, and do hereby strictly direct and require you to consult with him about the most proper measures for sending him safe home, and for that Purpose to send him with all his things to such of our Factorys up the River as to be nearest to and most convenient for him to gett to his own Country under the Care of some discreet Person whom you can confide in to see these our Orders duely put in Execution. He has likewise requested to us, That if any of his Religion should at any time be Sold to any of our Factors, That upon application for their Redemption and upon paying two other good Slaves for one, they may be restored to their Liberty, which we have agreed to, and do therefore recommend it to you to give the Necessary Orders to all our Factors up the River to pay due Obedience to the Same; and as it will be a great Satisfaction to his Friends and Benefactors here to be informed by Letters under his own hand of the Treatment he meets with from you and of his Safe Arrival in his own Country, you are to desire him to write to us by all opportunitys. We are

> *Your Loving Friends*
> *The Court of Assistants of the Royal*
> *African Co. of England'*

I would reread and reflect on the content of this letter many times during the voyage to Africa for there was much to ponder. I was pleasantly surprised, and a little embarrassed, by the compliments bestowed on me. I was happy to have been called a sober and ingenious person. And yet I could not help but feel somewhat saddened at still being described as a

'Black'. I had always regarded 'Blacks' – certainly those who did not share my faith – as being a different and much inferior race. I had come to realise that my new friends and associates in England meant no harm or insult in the use of this adjective; after all, they were unfamiliar with the complexities of people from a foreign land. And I had no desire to enter into debate or arguments for fear of appearing hostile or ungrateful. But that did not wipe away my deeply held view that 'Blacks' – like those savages who beat and captured me – were not related to me in any way.

The letter also gave me satisfaction and comfort in the way instructions had been given for my care, protection and safe passage. I regarded the wording as kindly and full of good intent. And yet I was only too aware that behind these instructions lay a broader, if only implied, purpose. There was an assumption that in return for this care and kindness, I would be a willing, and perhaps influential, ally in the company's trading ambition in my part of the world. Perhaps I was already compromised, for the letter was explicit in agreeing to a request that I had made in the light of my own experience; that should a person of my faith be captured and sold to the company, he or she should be freed in return for two other slaves.[32]

The company was anxious that we should weigh anchor and depart for Africa as quickly as possible, but Capt. Freeman was determined to take on more provisions and wait for more favourable winds. This prompted another rebuke. In a letter dated African House, July 11, a letter appearing to have been written in some haste, perhaps fury, Richard Spence let it be known that the Gentlemen of the Court were 'very much displeased' that the Dolphin had not sailed immediately the letters and instructions had been delivered. The secretary added, 'They order me to acquaint you therewith, and that they expect you will sail forthwith and make the best of your way the wind favouring you.'

Capt. Freeman was a man confident in his own opinions and maritime skills, however, so it was not until July 15 when he felt that conditions were right and that we were fully provisioned, that we finally set sail for Africa.

We made good progress in favourable winds, with a full set of sails set on our two masts driving us westwards down the widening Channel before rounding the island of Guernsey. While in England I came to appreciate that the great seaports of London, Bristol and Liverpool were the ones most associated with the trading and transportation of slaves. And now, while sailing these waters, not far from the French coast, I was told how the sea-fairing community of Guernsey, and its neighbouring island of Jersey, also profited from slaving activities through the involvement of prominent local seamen, the provision of ships, and the supply of goods and services.

One of the most influential seamen from these parts was Vice Admiral Sir George Carteret from Jersey who was a consultant to the Royal African Company. Indeed, he once had an apartment in African House where I had lodged. George Carteret was a founder of the Company of Royal Adventurers into Africa that was established in 1660 to trade in gold, ivory and slaves. One of the earliest voyages of that company was undertaken by Sir George's son James Carteret who, in 1663, collected 302 slaves from West Africa for transportation to the West Indies. Nine years later, the Royal African Company was formed to carry on the trading activities of the Royal Adventurers and in 1680 Sir George died having established reputations in both England and the American colonies. A man of the sea, Sir George had received little education, but he had risen to be a member of the Privy Council and one of the Lords of the Admiralty. I would have loved to have met this man.

In these waters, close to Guernsey and Jersey, we were on alert for skirmishes with the French navy, pirates and privateers, but happily our voyage continued unhindered. This passage was turning out to be far more enjoyable and productive than my previous voyages each way across the Atlantic Ocean. I was allowed to relax, to contemplate my future, attend to my devotions and improve my English skills in conversation with sailors and the few fellow passengers on board, employees of the Royal African Company who, I was happy to witness, accepted me on their own terms. Thanks to Capt. Freemen, I seem to have acquired a reputation and status that was rewarded with respect and some admiration.

We continued to make good progress, untroubled by storms or, perhaps worse, becalming conditions. Soon we were off the African coast, passing the Canary Islands, once known as 'the Fortunate Isles' but in these more modern times recognised more for supporting the conquering Spanish navy as well as traders, missionaries, and pirates. We crossed the Tropic of Cancer in the knowledge that to the east lay the great hot desert of the Sahara. I could tell by the warming air that I was nearing my homeland.

On August 7, a little more than three weeks after departing the Isle of Wight, we spotted the muddied waters of the Gambia estuary with Barrah Point and Banian Point lying on opposing shorelines at the entrance. A kindly seaman, used to these waters, pointed out the distinctive wooded clump of trees above Barrah Point.

'We always look out for those trees,' he said. 'Sailors and explorers have always known that place as The Pavilion, because of its shape,' he continued, perhaps realising that I probably missed this feature on my outward voyage.

'Thanks,' I said. 'It feels good to be back in the Gambia.'

The *Dolphin* sailed past Dog Island off the northern shore of the estuary and came to anchor off James Island, the very place that my enslaved state was confirmed, and I was shipped to Maryland so many sunrises, so many moons ago. I was keen to step ashore, but surprisingly I felt fully at ease. I was home and miraculously I was already beginning to experience the feelings and rhythms of my traditional life flowing through my veins.

I was home!

I am not ashamed to say that I had tears in my eyes as I looked out over the fort with all its bustling activity. I could not help but reflect how I had left this place as a common slave, tethered to other captives in deplorable conditions and reduced to a state of total desolation. That was just four years ago. And now I had returned, travelling in some comfort as a freed man, a man of substance with valuable possessions – gifts from the most influential people in English society who had also provided me with experiences that I could not have imagined in my modest home in Bondu. But what of my family and friends, back home in that community? I wondered how I would find my father and mother, my dear wives and children. I had been starved of news from home and I was now even more anxious to return.

My mind was still in great turmoil when, late that night, the ship sent ashore its longboat with the *Dolphin*'s papers confirming our passengers and cargo. Unfortunately, despite my impatience, I was made to stay on board with everyone else. There were formalities to perform.

At noon the following day, nine guns were fired from the fort in salute of our arrival. This was acknowledged by nine of our guns firing in return. Then, at last, Capt. Freeman, myself, four clerks and an apprentice from the company, were ferried to the island to be met at the jetty by a crowd of soldiers and company representatives. Officers from the company who were there to greet me made every effort to make me feel welcome and at ease.

I was provided with my own room in the fort's living quarters. When it was found that I was lacking bedding, it was immediately arranged that sheets should be found for me. It was plain to me that orders had been given to treat me well. For myself I had but one ambition: to send immediate messages to my family, giving them news of my safe return. But it was explained to me that it would be easier and quicker for messages to be sent overland from the company's factories much further upstream. I was encouraged to be patient while preparations were made.

On a hot December day in 1734 I felt moved to write to Nathaniel Brassey to inform him that I was in good health and had arrived safely – 'praise be to God for it' – at James Fort. I told him that all the Muslims of my acquaintance prayed for his health, long life and prosperity for the many good services he had done me. I concluded by expressing hope that 'all your good family is well' and conveying 'respects to all friends, especially to the young Miss Gray', an attractive young woman with whom I had shared several pleasant conversations.

That enforced stay in the fort seemed like a punishment, although I recognised that arrangements were being made as quickly as possible. Certainly, I was being treated well with the greatest kindness and civility.

One of those who had been on the jetty to greet me was Francis Moore, one of the company's officers who, having joined as a clerk (or writer, as such employees were styled), was now serving in a higher capacity as an agent (or factor to give him his proper title). We quickly took a great liking to each other as we talked about our experiences both in Africa

Portrait of Ayuba Suleiman Diallo by William Hoare of Bath R.A. Private
Collection Photo © Christie's Images/Bridgeman Images

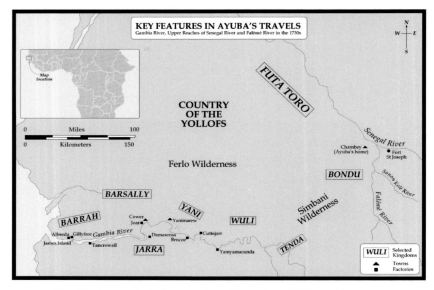

Simplified map of the Senegal/Gambia region of West Africa in the 1730s, indicating some of the kingdoms and settlements known to Ayuba Suleiman Diallo.

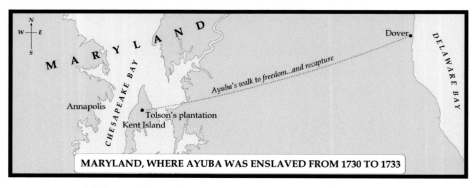

Simplified map of Maryland, Ayuba's place of enslavement and the route of his walk to freedom and recapture.

Part of a letter from Ayuba Suleiman Diallo to his father, written while he was enslaved in Maryland. In this letter, written in Arabic, Diallo states: 'There is no good in the country of the Christians for a Muslim'. Announcing to 'all the Muslims of Bondu' that he is alive, he appeals to the rulers of the country and his family to ensure that his two wives do not remarry. ©The British Library Board. Add MS 20783a.

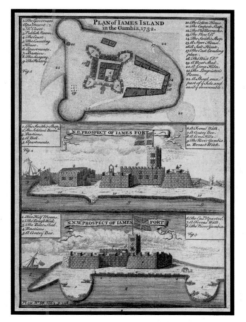

Plan of James Island (renamed Kunta Kinteh Island in 2011) on the Gambia river in 1732 with views of the fort from the north east and north, north west, by Jacques Nicolas Bellin. The engraving/etching was published in Histoire Générale des Voyages, ou nouvelle collection de toutes les relations de voyages par mer et par terre, Paris, 1759. Copyright © Stanford University. All Rights Reserved.

A view of Limehouse in 1751 by engraver John Boydell. The view, taken
near Limehouse Bridge, contains few vessels but depicts several landing
places at low water. ©National Maritime Museum, Greenwich, London.
Green Blackwall Collection.

A perspective view of the South Front of Kensington Palace, taken from
the end of the slope of the great Walk. Print published in 1744 by Anthony
Highmore. ©The Trustees of the British Museum.

A Koran written by Ayuba Suleiman Diallo, featuring his portrait, 1734, on display in West Africa: Word, Symbol, Song and from the collection of Mr Rami El-Nimer for Arts and Culture. The portrait is annotated with handwritten words 'Job, Son of Soliman Dgiallo, High Priest of Bonda, in the Country of Foota, Africa.' The engraved portrait which was added to the text after it was completed, is based on an oil painting by British painter William Hoare. The Koran, with its portrait, is part of the El-Nimer Collection, Beirut.

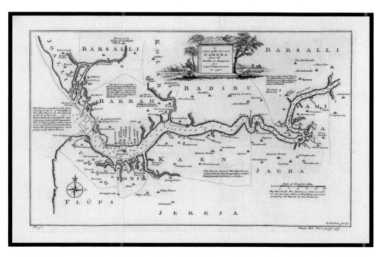

Detailed map of the Gambra (Gambia) River and its tributaries, dated 1732, published in A New General Collection of Voyages and Travels, compiled by John Green. The map extends from the Atlantic to Eropina, identifying several towns, factories and other details including soundings within the river. The map illustrates the exploration of Capt John Leach, on behalf of the Royal African Company. Leach and Thomas Harrison explored the Gambia River in 1732 in search of new trading opportunities. ©2018 Barry Lawrence Ruderman Antique Maps Inc., 7463 Girard Avenue, La Jolla, CA 92037, United States.

'The Man with spear on a galloping horse' is Boomey Haman Seaca, King of Barsally, as depicted in Travels into the Inland Parts of Africa by Ayuba's companion, Francis Moore and published in 1738. Moore records that Haman Seaca's horse was 'milk white', 16 hands high with a long mane and a tail that swept the ground. His bridle was of a bright red leather, plated with silver in the Moorish manner. His saddle was in the same style, with a high pommel. This illustration was provided by the Schomburg Center for Research in Black Culture, Manuscripts, Archives and Rare Books Division. The New York Public Library Digital Collections.

The River Thames with Montagu House, from near Westminster Bridge, London. Painting by Samuel Scott (c1702-1772). ©Guildhall Art Gallery, City of London Corporation.

Portrait of Sir Hans Sloane, Bt., by Stephen Slaughter, 1736. ©National Portrait Gallery, London.

Portrait of King George II from the studio of Charles Jervas, circa 1727, the year of his coronation. ©National Portrait Gallery, London.

Portrait of Queen Caroline of Brandenburg-Ansbach, from the studio of Charles Jervas in 1727, the year of her coronation. ©National Portrait Gallery, London.

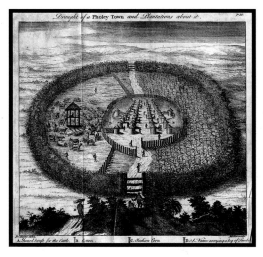

Plan of a Fula township and plantations from Travels into the Inland Parts of Africa by Francis Moore, 1738. Depicted are a guard house for protecting cattle (centre left, marked A); cotton plantations (in the margins of the inner circle, marked B); Indian corn plantation in the right hemisphere, marked C); and a man carrying timber (bottom left, marked D). Illustrations provided by Schomburg Center for Research in Black Culture, Manuscripts, Archives and Rare Books Division, The New York Public Library. (1738). Draught of a Pholey Town and Plantations about it. New York Public Library Digital Collections.

and in London. I was greatly impressed with Mr Moore's knowledge of the Gambia region and it served him well that he was so enthusiastic to add to his experience and education.

At last, some two weeks after my arrival, we finally set sail from James Island in *Flame*, a sloop of the type of vessel used to navigate the higher reaches of the river. As was the custom, our vessel of some thirty tons saluted the fort with five guns and we received a five-gun salute in return. Our ship was heavily laden with goods that Mr Moore needed to restock the factory at Joar, as well as my own considerable collection of gifts.

Just prior to our departure, Mr Moore had learnt that he had been promoted to be the Chief Factor at Joar. His letter of appointment was signed 'Your Loving Friends' by Richard Hull and Hugh Hamilton, the company's chief merchants. That letter also gave instructions about my treatment, as Mr Moore, in our new-found friendship, had kindly shown me. It read, 'By this Conveyance comes one Black Free Man, by Name Job Ben Solomon; whom you are to use with the greatest Respect, and all the Civility you possibly can.'

'What do you think of that?' Mr Moore asked me.

I just smiled in reply, preferring to keep my thoughts private.

Maybe Mr Moore read my thoughts, for he then said, 'But Job, I promise you I am not treating you with respect and civility just because of orders. I genuinely like and admire you. I hope we can share true friendship.'

This kind reply prompted me to raise another issue that had been troubling me. 'Have you received any news of my loyal companion, Lamine Ndiaye, who was also captured and enslaved?' I enquired.

'I'm sorry,' he replied. 'I have no news to give you. But I will do my best to obtain word as to his whereabouts and well-being.'

Our initial voyage upriver was slow, the level and flow of water having risen as a result of recent rains, and it was not until August 26 that we reached the creek leading to the Damasensa trading post in the Jarra kingdom. Leaving *Flame* moored in the river, Mr Moore and I took to a yawl and ventured up the narrow creek. I think Mr Moore was hoping that we might meet some of my friends and acquaintances so that the news could spread about my freedom and well-being.

After about half a mile we saw several blue and red monkeys high up in the trees, leaping extraordinary distances from one branch to another. I was impressed that Mr Moore had already learnt from local people that these agile monkeys, already familiar to me, lived almost entirely high up in the trees and hardly ever set foot on the ground.

That evening in Damasensa, while we were sat under a great tree, we talked more about my past life and capture. I admitted that I was feeling uneasy, as we were seated close by the very spot that my servant Lamine Ndiaye and I had been brutally attacked and captured by that evil Mandingo band of robbers. And then something truly extraordinary happened.

As if predetermined by Allah himself, six or seven of the same men who had carried out that attack strolled by, hardly noticing our existence. My composure snapped. I was beside myself with suppressed rage and fury; I could barely control myself. I was ready to kill each and every one these, using the pistols and broadsword with which I had armed myself for protection.

Fortunately, Mr Moore displayed more restraint and sense, recognising that our chance of escaping with our own lives from such an encounter would be slim. We sat quietly, waiting to see if they recognised me.

My stomach was churning inside as I looked into their eyes for any sign of recognition. But there was none. Their manner was one of quiet good humour. They showed no malice.

Mr Moore persuaded me to call over the men and question them about the circumstances of my capture without me betraying to them my identity. The tension was defused, as the men recounted truthfully, and in apparent innocence, what had happened that dreadful day.

I then asked what had happened to their king and was told he had been killed in strange circumstances. Among the goods he had been given by Capt. Pike as the price for me and Lamine Ndiaye was a pistol he commonly wore strung round his neck. The pistol was always loaded. Then one day the pistol had gone off, accidently firing a ball into the king's throat and killing him instantly.

I was so overcome with this news that I fell to my knees and thanked Mohammed for making the King of Jarra die by the very goods for which he had sold me into slavery.

'Mr Moore, you see how God Almighty was displeased at this man's making me a slave. He therefore made him die by the very pistol for which he sold me,' I exclaimed. 'Yet I ought to forgive him, because had I not been sold, I should neither have known anything of the English tongue, nor have had any of the fine, useful and valuable things I have carried here. Nor would I have known that in the world there is such a place as England...' I was in full flow now as I examined the paradoxes of my situation: 'Nor such noble, good and generous people as Queen Caroline, Prince William, the Duke of Montagu, the Earl of Pembroke, Mr Holden, Mr Oglethorpe and the Royal African Company.'

I could not imagine then that Queen Caroline, whom I so admired, would continue her great work for only a little longer. Much later, I received the sad news that she died at the end of 1737, leaving King George and her nation in deep mourning.

Now, at peace with myself and my enemies, I felt able

to reflect how if now I was able to meet that King of Jarra, I would have done all I could to have saved his life. Turning to Mr Moore I said quietly, 'I now see that it was not the Mandingoes but God who had led me into strange lands.'

And in this mood of contentment I felt able to continue my journey in the company of Mr Moore, whom I had come to admire even more greatly.

We continued our journey upstream, arriving on September 1 at Joar, the trading post and factory where I had been enslaved and sold to Capt. Pike. It was a place full of dark memories. Yet on this occasion, accepted as to my proper station in life, I was treated with every courtesy. Mr Moore took no time in seeking out a Fula who knew my father. He expressed great joy at seeing me safely returned from slavery. This man was then engaged to deliver a message to my father, informing him of my well-being. But I insisted that my father should be urged not to travel to meet me.

'It is fitting for the young to go to the old, and not the old to come to the young,' I explained.

I then provided the Fula with messages and presents for my wives and asked that he should return with Fatimah, my youngest, best-loved child.

While waiting for the messenger to return, I passed the time accompanying Mr Moore on his trading visits to Cower and several other places in the area where I could describe my experiences and speak of the power of the English. Mr Moore seemed pleased, for he explained I dispelled much of the horror felt by Fula regarding the state of slavery among the English.

'They generally imagine that all who are sold for slaves are either eaten or murdered, since none ever return,' he said.

I also took the opportunity of trading on my own account, selling some of the presents that I had been given in England

and buying a young slave woman and two horses in readiness for my return to Bondu. I also gave to the Fula people a good deal of writing paper, provided by the Royal African Company, which I knew would be regarded as an extremely useful commodity.

I was aware it would take the Fula messenger some time to travel to my father in Bondu and then return to Joar, so I asked if I could return to James Island to collect the remaining, greater part of the goods that I had brought from England. It so happened that the *Flame* was about to make the same journey, carrying a cargo of corn required at the fort. We left on September 26 with Mr Moore giving orders to the master to show me 'every respect he could'. Mr Moore also promised me that he would send word as soon as the messenger return from Bondu and that if there was a mishap, other messengers would be sent.

On my arrival back at James Island, I settled for waiting on news from Bondu. Time hung heavily, even though I occupied myself examining and admiring the many gifts that had been given me. Days of waiting became weeks. I met often with Richard Hull – who was the Governor at Fort James – and Charles Orfeur, both of whom were extremely kind to me and seemed willing to help in any way they could.

I suggested that I should make the journey on my own back to Bondu and my family but was advised against such a venture, given the uncertain safety in the area, and both gentlemen urged me to wait for replies from the messengers already dispatched. On November 13 Mr Hull sent a letter to Mr Moore, in which he asked to be informed about the response to messages sent to my friends informing them of my return.

On December 3 my hopes rose when I saw *Flame* arriving at the fort. On board was Mr Moore, along with twelve slaves.

We greeted each other, and I learnt he had been ill with a 'violent cold' and 'swollen throat'. Sadly, he carried no news about the messengers. I was urged to remain patient.

While I waited, I sent out several letters, fulfilling a promise I had made before my departure from London.

One was written to Sir Hans Sloane that I set down in both Arabic and English. Dated December 8 with an address of 'James Fort Rio Gambia', the letter was intended to reassure Sir Hans that I was in good health and being well looked after by Governor Hull and Mr Orfeur while I waited for a response to messages dispatched to family and friends.

I also expressed my gratitude to Sir Hans, explaining that, 'You have done a great favour... and are my best friend, and I wish you a long life... I always remember you... You have been as a Father to me.' I then sent my best wishes as a Muslim who loved him 'very heartily' and prayed for him. 'I wish God may bless you... I wish from my heart all that you have may prosper.'

On the same day, I set down a letter in similar vein to Mr John Chandler whom I had befriended in London, thanks again to Sir Hans Sloane. Mr Chandler was an eminent apothecary working in King Street, in London's Cheapside and I was grateful that he and his family had taken a keen interest in me and had done much to put me at my ease.[33] My letter, written in Arabic, assured Mr Chandler that 'I give my service to you with all my heart.' The letter continued, 'I am very well but am not yet gone home but still remain at James Fort, Gambia but I hope I shall go very soon. You are a good man and I pray for you with all my heart and I wish your family all well and I love you very well.' I sent my good wishes 'to all my friends, your wife, and little miss and master and I wish you long life and happiness'. I repeated my sentiments about Governor Hull, expressed in my letter to

Sir Hans Sloane, stating the Governor was a 'very good man' who was taking 'very good care of me'.

As the days passed, the fort gradually took on a festive air as the company's officers, staff and slaves prepared for their Christmas celebrations. Still there was no news from family or friends to lighten my spirits. But now I had a new companion, a young clerk called Thomas Hilton, who had arrived from Holland earlier that month on the company's snow, the *Success*. Mr Hilton had been assigned as an assistant to Mr Moore.

The day after Christmas, on December 26, the three of us joined the sloop *Flame* for Joar, taking with us some of the goods that I had brought from England. The vessel was making a trading mission upriver under the master, John Brown accompanied by Mr James Connor, a company factor.

On the first of January, we halted alongside Elephant's Island, below Damasensa, to wait for the flood tide, when Mr Moore received news that there had been a family feud in which the King of Barsally had been confronted by one of his brothers, Boomey Haman Seaca. Mr Moore was told that in the skirmish which had advanced on Joar, almost everyone had fled, including the staff and servants at the company's factory which now lay undefended. Mr Moore acted with some bravery in my opinion, for he immediately hired a canoe with a crew of three men to carry him to Joar to check on the factory and its people.

When Mr Moore arrived at Joar the next day, he did indeed find that many villagers had fled, but the factory and stores were still intact and in good order. Some ten people were found sheltering and unharmed in the company's house. Mr Moore discovering that the Boomey Haman Seaca was at Sanjally, a town some half day's journey away, dispatched a messenger with presents, including brandy from the company.

Mr Moore was well aware that the king and his brothers had a particular thirst for brandy. The following day the messenger returned with a handsome friendly message and an assurance that white men – especially Mr Moore – would not be harmed.

Boomey Haman Seaca recalled a previous encounter with Mr Moore in the very same town, back in 1731. Along with his father, the then king, and his two brothers, Boomey Haman Benda and Boomey Loyi Eminga, Boomey Haman Seaca had marched into Joar with several hundred men, both mounted and on foot. For several days the ruling family and their followers indulged themselves, drinking brandy in a drunken state. The king and his brothers may have been Mohammadans, but they were of quite another persuasion to we Marabouts who would never countenance indulging in drink.

Sadly, around this time, while on board *Flame*, Mr Hilton had had been taken ill with a fever and after a period of ten days, he died on January 21. He had been in this land just forty-one days. He was buried very decently under an orange tree in the garden of the Joar factory. A messenger was sent to Fort James with an account of his death and his effects, together with the favourable message received from Boomey Haman Seaca.

Meanwhile, given my concern about the dangers that seemed to exist in and around Joar, I had asked Mr Connor if I could be put ashore with my possessions at a small community called Indea, about six miles above Damasensa, where I felt I would be made welcome and kept in safety. There I stayed until January 29 when, on receiving news there was no further danger in Joar, I took a canoe to rejoin Mr Moore on board *Flame*. I did what I could to assist as the company representatives went about their business.

Then, on the fateful day of Friday, February 14, 1735, one of the messengers who had been sent to Bondu returned with some of my most-loved acquaintances, bearing the dread news that my father had died some time ago. I was distraught; overcome with grief. No wonder there had been no reply to my letters and entreaties. What punishment for my wanton disobedience; for crossing the river contrary to his wise entreaties.

As if to ease my pain, I was told that my father had received letters that I had sent from England informing him of my freedom and the status that had been granted me by influential people in that country. At least that was some consolation.

But that was not all. I was delivered news that in my prolonged absence, one of my wives had married another man who, on hearing about my return, had thought it wise to run away. And to complete this black picture, I was told that in my absence abroad there had been a dreadful war in my country and that not so much as a single cow remained of our large and valuable herd of cattle. My town, my community, the whole kingdom had been caught up in the long-standing feud between two competing dynasties, both based in Futa Toro: the Sisibe and the Denianke.

By all accounts, Maka Bubu Malik Si, leader of the Sisibe family, had gathered his Fulani warriors in Futa Toro to regain power over my homeland in one of the periodic wars of dynastic squabbles. My family and our community had always remained loyal to the Denianke dynasty in Futa Toro and had steadfastly refused to recognise the rights of their rival in Bondu, Maka Bubu Malik Si and, before him, his father Malik Si.

I was aware in my early years of manhood that these rivalries existed, but with our work, especially trading, being largely untroubled and rewarding, such dynastic disagreements seemed of little consequence. It seems that while I was away from home, facing my own personal challenges, the Sisibe had flexed their muscles over the weaker Denianke and had rampaged through much of Bondu. It left my homeland in tatters.[34]

My hopes of a happy return and a joyous reunion with my family and friends were shattered. I was beside myself. I wept uncontrollably for the loss of my father and the devastation heaped on my community. For three or four days, I was comforted in continuous conversation with my colleagues as we shared our different experiences – good and bad – over the past few years. And as I came to terms with what had passed, I felt able to forgive my wife, and the man who had taken her. After all, who could blame them? My wife could not help but think I was dead, for I had been taken to a land from whence no Fula had ever returned.

I was anxious to return to my community, and yet I felt in my soul that I was not yet ready to make that journey. For some reason I was still finding it difficult to adjust to this way of life: the sights, sounds, smells – and heat – that were once so familiar and natural in my past life. These sensations were in such sharp contrast to those that I had encountered, and experienced, back in England. Africa and England seemed worlds apart.

'Where do I belong?' I asked Mr Moore while in one of these reflective moods.

'Here, Job. This is your home, your people, your heritage,' he replied in measured tone, adding, 'But I'm confident that you will bring some of the benefits of your experiences to your people in Bondu.'

There were other reasons for staying a little longer in Joar. I needed more time to reflect, to think and to pray. And I was still anxiously waiting for news of my trusted guide and interpreter, Lamine Ndiaye.

I was also eager to learn more about trading activities and where I could be of assistance, to the benefit of both my

community and the company. I had already received some
instructions, such as the need to report distances in British
miles. Very soon that trading opportunity would arise. But
first I had to endure yet another farewell, this time one that
deeply saddened me.

I learnt that Mr Moore would soon be leaving to return
home, and that his place as Chief Factor would be taken by
Thomas Johnson, who had arrived in Joar with the Governor
on the company's sloop, *James*. The news upset me greatly,
for I had established a strong bond with Mr Moore, whom I
trusted and valued as a friend.

Mr Moore agreed to carry with him to England several
letters that, with his great assistance, I had written to the Royal
African Company and several of my English acquaintances. In
a note to Sir Hans Sloane I included a gift of some poisoned
arrows I had managed to collect, knowing that these would
be of great interest to him, as well as his medical assistant, Dr
Mortimer. Other letters were sent to James Oglethorpe and
His Grace, the Duke of Montagu.

The letter to the Duke was dated Joar Factory, April 5 and
expressed, with Mr Moore's great assistance, my sentiments
and appreciation to all those who had been so kind to me:

> *'This comes to give my duty to your Grace, praying
> God to bless you for what you have done for me. All
> the Mussulmen here pray for you. This comes by Mr
> Moore, late a factor in the Company's Service, who
> came up hither along with me, and has taken a great
> deal of care of me, and used me as his Brother, for
> which I should be glad to hear of your doing good
> for him. I am still in Gambia; have heard news from
> Bundu that my Father is dead, and one of my Wives
> married, the Bearer will inform you more of my Affairs*

than anybody else, he having been here trading for the Company these six or seven months. My duty to the King and Queen and all the Royal Family. I heartily pray to God to bless your Grace. . . P.S. I hope your Grace will not forget my Servant and fellow Slave who is in Maryland.'

Three days after writing this letter for me, Mr Moore departed downstream for James Island on board the *James*. He seemed in high spirits. I joined the Governor and others to bid farewell, bearing a far different countenance. I was in an emotional state, having said my goodbyes, and handed over the letters for England. After all, we had remained together since my return to Gambia. I beseeched Mr Moore to extend my fondest good wishes to my acquaintances and to tell them that I would send them longer letters once I had gained a greater mastery of the English tongue.

I gave an assurance to Mr Moore that I would endeavour to spend my days assisting the English in return for my redemption from slavery and the innumerable favours so freely given.

I also gave Mr Moore an undertaking that the very next day I would be travelling with Mr Thomas Hull, nephew of the Governor, up to Yanimarew and the gum forest, to help explain how trading gum with the company would benefit both the people of that area and the English nation.

Mr Moore had explained to me that a great deal of Gum Sanaga was exported each year to England, almost all of it provided by French traders. This gum was especially important for the growing textile industry. The Ferlo forest, on the western boundary of Bondu that I would be visiting with Mr Hull, was abundant with trees that produced very fine white Gum Arabic. This forest, laying some five days' journey from

Yanimarew travelling north of the Gambia, was contained in largely uninhabited land shared by the people of Yany and Futa Toro. Mr Moore was hopeful that as my own country lay on the edge of the forest, I would express a good opinion of the English to the people of that region and hopefully prevail on them to trade with the Royal African Company, and thus offer competition with the French.

'It is the least I can do,' I said as we embraced for the last time.

CHAPTER 8

Travels through a war-torn country

◇◇◇

It was on the next day, May 9, that Thomas Hull and I set out on my first trading mission. Mr Hull, while still young, was already an experienced company officer. He had arrived in Gambia as a writer in May 1733 and served at Fort James and Brucoe before taking charge of the Joar factory. And he quickly showed himself to be an intrepid traveller, strong in body but, surprisingly, somewhat lacking in conversation and curiosity. Fortunately, he had been instructed to keep a journal, largely as an aid for those who might be engaged in further expeditions.

For the sake of clarity, I have based the following account in diary form, using Mr Hull's notes, as well as my own recollection.

Wednesday May 9, 1735

The initial phase of our journey was made by a shallow-bottom boat that took us from Joar, upstream the River Gambia. We meandered past Deer Island, Baboon Island and other islands nestling in bends in the narrowing river, passing the trading posts at Brucoe and Cuttejarr, until we reached the Yamyamacunda factory on the bank of the river. I knew this to be one of the main factories for trading in slaves and ivory. Here we rested and took on provisions for the next overland stage of our journey.

Saturday June 14

At first light we moved on.

To support us on our mission, Thomas Hull had hired three messengers: a native black servant and two guides who had been recruited in the kingdom of Wuli which lay to the north and on the other side of the Gambia River. We also had horses and an ass to carry our load. (We should have had two asses, but one fell ill just before we left.)

At seven o'clock the animals were sent across the river and at midday Mr Hull and his support team made the crossing. I had already crossed to make my own way to the Sandu village of Cobas, some four miles north of Yamyamacunda, in an area that was familiar to me. The rest of the party arrived with their loaded animals in the village later in the afternoon. And here we rested, visited by a local trading chief who told us that the night before a girl in a nearby Fula village had been killed by lightning. It was a sobering reminder that the rainy season had started.

Sunday June 15

As expected, we woke early this morning to find torrential rain falling from the blackened sky. This delayed our intended departure, but as was the nature of this season, by ten o'clock the rain had cleared, and we were ready to continue our journey. By now we had recruited extra help – guides, bearers and messengers – along with additional animals, so that we were eighteen in number setting off for Moncodaway, some ten miles away to the east. On arrival, we could not be but moved by the saddened state of this once-thriving township. What once had been a sizeable, strong community had been largely destroyed by fire the year before. Even so, we still managed to find sufficient accommodation to pass the night there in reasonable comfort.

Monday June 16

This morning we set out at six o'clock and travelled hard, covering twelve miles in just six hours, to reach the large town of Suncabar by noon. We all rested and sheltered from the midday heat until three o'clock in the afternoon. While we relaxed, we discussed a feature on the landscape that was new to me. During our journey we had passed by a hill, which featured on its summit some large, plain stones. Around these stones were impressions, like footprints. Mr Hull had asked about this place on his arrival in Suncabar and was told the so-called footprints had been made by a King of Cabbah who had visited the hill to engage in a battle. Mr Hull, who recorded this anecdote in his journal, decided that he and most of the party should make the most of the good weather and continue their journey to Congcord, six miles to the north-east.

However, I was left behind with two helpers to tend to one of our asses that had become sick and given instructions to rejoin Mr Hull as soon as possible. Consequently, I rested overnight in Suncabar.

Tuesday June 17

Our small party left very early this morning, arriving in

Congcord, the capital town in Wuli, at about eight o'clock. As we rejoined Mr Hull and the rest of the group, I was again saddened to see that Congcord, once an important and thriving town, had been ravished by decay, the result of various wars among neighbouring people.

Despite our considerable exertion to rejoin our expedition, I was anxious to move on to be closer to my community in Bondu. But it was not to be. Mr Hull had been informed that we could not move on until Endeney Seca, the Governor of Congcord, had given permission for us to proceed through the kingdom. It transpired that we would remain for the next three days to complete the various formalities.

Within an hour of my arrival in the town, Mr Hull led our party to the town's meeting house where we were received by Endeney Seca; his younger brothers, Nackwood and Samba; and many people of Congcord. Endeney Seca was a man of small stature and mature age. But we also found him to be a leader with an air of obvious authority while still possessing a pleasant nature. Mr Hull dutifully saluted the Governor with seven guns and gave him a present that John Cooper, the factor at Yamyamacunda, had provided for the King of Wuli.

Wednesday June 18 and Thursday June 19
These two days were devoted to discussion, with trade being the leading topic of conversation, feasting and entertainment. But first we were again thanked for the gift that we had presented and in return the Governor promised Mr Hull the gift of a cow.

We had much to discuss. I know that Mr Hull was especially pleased to learn that there was an abundance of elephants in Wuli, which indicated a potentially valuable trade in ivory. We were even given the good news that at that very moment traders from the neighbouring kingdom of Tenda were on the way to the Royal African Company's factory in Yamyamacunda with trading goods of elephants' teeth and gold.

The Governor himself told Mr Hull how proud he was that the company was considering establishing a factory in his country. Everyone who brought trade through Wuli would be welcome, he said, adding that as a sign of good faith he would send a 'man of note' with traders to ensure safe passage to Yamyamacunda. As confirmation of the warmth of Congcord's hospitality, we were honoured with an entertaining display of energetic dancing, performed by many young girls of the town.

While we were waiting for permission to move on, we took steps to replenish our stores of food. Unfortunately, corn and rice were exceedingly scarce, and we were unable to buy any, even though we offered generous terms. The shortage of grain seemed to be in sharp contrast to the availability of meat, for there were plenty of animals, especially goats and lizards, running about the houses in the town. Fortunately, I was able to buy an ass to help carry our supplies.

Finally, we were joined at supper on our third evening in Congcord by the Governor, who informed us that all formalities had been completed and we should set out the next morning.

Friday June 20
Not wishing to waste any further time, our party – fifteen in number – set out at seven o'clock in the morning, continuing our journey in a north-easterly direction. We stopped to rest awhile at a large Muslim community called Cohunt, eight miles north-east from Congcord, before continuing to Sowro, another township ravaged by war. We were told the town had been burnt in the last fight with the Wulis. After a day's journey of some fifteen miles we were tired and hungry, but sadly there was little grain to be found in this pitiful place. We

contented ourselves with consuming provisions we had carried and settled for fitful sleep.

Saturday June 21 and Sunday June 22

Fortunately, after another hard day of fifteen miles' travel, we reached Canophy. Along the way we passed through Colingding, another town that had been ravaged by war. After taking a rest we continued to Canophy where, thankfully, we were able to buy rice, paying in silver. Here, in this sizeable town, we spent much of our time cleaning and cooking the rice, as well as resting.

Monday June 23

Today our progress was frustrated by another delay. The day started well, as we were able to set off at five-thirty in the morning for our journey to Condery, just eight miles away. We made good time and were anxious to travel on. Unfortunately, we were forced to halt and spend the night here because we had to wait for the master of a large town called Cassang, further eastwards along our route, to give us his permission to proceed. I am sure Mr Hull must be wondering why there are so many leaders in this kingdom ruling over individual communities, often of quite modest size.

The way of our people, based on the authority of local leaders respected in their local communities, may seem so different from the system of government back in England; but I wonder whether this is so. My English education taught me little about how people were governed in England; only there appeared to be many grand, and very rich, leaders in authority.

Tuesday June 24 and Wednesday June 25

In contrast to the previous day, we started early at about five o'clock, and had an excellent day's travel, covering sixteen miles, including the crossing of a large creek, which we were told flowed into the River Samy with its fearsome reputation for being the home of many crocodiles. We arrived at the thriving township of Calore at about one o'clock in the afternoon and Mr Hull decided we should stay here so that I might buy some corn to replenish diminishing stores. Thankfully I was successful in this task.

Mr Hull expressed some surprise when he discovered that everyone in the town, including the Master himself – Bucar Mancah – had been slaves belonging to the late King of Wuli.

It was clear that our arrival had caused some excitement in the community for, at about four o'clock, the people welcomed us in boisterous fashion, entertaining us with a ceremony that involved much merrymaking, including the beating of drums, mock battles and dancing.

The people of Calore were also intrigued, for it was apparent no-one in the town had ever seen or heard of a white man like Mr Hull. Much to my amusement, women seemed so fearful of Mr Hull's colour that they refused to go near him. Happily, I found that the women showed no such inhibitions where I was concerned.

All our party rested well that night, appreciative of the good-natured welcome that we had received in this community. And it was fortunate that the people were hospitable, because torrential rain forced us to remain in Calore for the whole of the next day and night as well.

Thursday June 26 and Friday June 27

Thankfully, the weather improved this morning, enabling us to travel the nine miles north-east to the town of Cambey, the last significant habitation in the kingdom of Wuli.

Here we spent a further day preparing for the next, challenging part of our journey – a four days' trek through an area known as the wilderness that separates Wuli and my homeland of Bondu. It is a forbidding place; a largely uninhabited region of woodlands and sandy scrub, crisscrossed by rivers and streams. There was a good deal of apprehension within our group, for the dangers that existed in the wilderness were well known, if not through experience but certainly from reputation.

The area abounds with many dangerous animals, including herds of elephants. As if to emphasise the point, the people of Cambey showed us a large quantity of elephants' teeth that was about to be carried to the Yamyamacunda factory.

The threat of robbers and bandits hidden among the undergrowth waiting to pounce on unsuspecting travellers was also raised during our discussions. Perhaps not surprisingly, Mr Hull was unsuccessful in his attempt to hire a guide familiar with this region, although the reason given was that all the men of the town were hard at work.

But at least I managed to replace a miserable horse I would leave behind with an ass that was both healthier and more obliging.

Saturday June 28 to Tuesday July 1
We set off at nine o'clock this Saturday morning, even though it was pouring with rain. We were now a party of fourteen, as a guide who had accompanied us from Congcord, Tobaubo Manso, returned to his community carrying with him letters from Mr Hull for Yamyamacunda.

At around midday we arrived at Bajarah, a creek seven miles to the east of Cambey. Here we rested for three or four hours before continuing our journey. We had hardly travelled a mile before it started to rain hard.

We knew there would be little respite from the weather and there would be little overnight shelter other than what we could construct ourselves from limbs of trees and vegetation. But both Mr Hull and I were determined to press on.

'We must just make the best of it,' said Mr Hull, recording much the same philosophy in his journal.

Mindful of the dangers, Mr Hull insisted that we would stay safe, provided we looked out for each other and took every precaution while resting or seeking fresh water supplies. Guards would be posted while others slept or undertook domestic duties.

We travelled hard through the wilderness, for Mr Hull informed us our journey would cover no less than sixty-five miles. On the second and third day we rose very early so that we could be travelling while taking advantage of the brilliant moonlight and coolness of the morning. On the fourth day – the Tuesday – heavy rain delayed our departure, but we were still able to set out at five o'clock. Late that morning we stopped by a wooded creek to prepare rice for our midday meal, the last of our fowl having been eaten the night before. After eating and resting we set off again for the final six-mile trek to the edge of the wilderness.

While it is true we were never able to discard our sense of apprehension, it must be recorded that our progress through this notorious land was largely unhindered by trouble. We were aware that for the observant traveller there were always signs indicating caution, such as the remains of an extinguished fire or the placement of some small fragments of cloth, maybe hanging from branches of a tree, as a signpost or indicator of a nearby source of water.

Throughout the journey we crossed with a good deal of ingenuity and exertion many creeks and rivers, including the Samy and Galore rivers, all of which were in full flood, given this was the rainy season. As planned, we also encountered a large pond called Sittadella. This was full, with ample water, but Mr Hull said he had been told it never dried completely, even in the dry season.

Finally, at the end of this wilderness, we crossed the River Yarico. It was here we could see in the distance the buildings of Goodery, a place I knew well, for it is the first town in my beloved Bondu country. It is hard to describe what my feelings were. Exhausted from this challenging part of our journey, I experienced mixed emotions: excitement and relief at returning after more than four years to my familiar land, and yet deep apprehension about what I might eventually find in my own township.

Would my family and friends be safe and well, and would they be happy to see me? So much had happened to me in these past few years – unbelievable things – and yet I was sure that what I would find would be the same as what I had left. Would my simple but warm and comforting community now be transformed in my eyes into a primitive and uncomfortable township, given all the bright and beguiling sights I had experienced during my time in England? And above all else, would I be accepted and treated with respect; forgiven for my past stupidities? I was now in a state of bewilderment and, surprisingly, deep apprehension.

I thought it prudent to dispatch a messenger into Bondu to inform friends and, hopefully, family of my arrival in this country.

Wednesday July 2 and Thursday July 3

We remained two full days in Goodery, resting and sheltering from the hot sun and awaiting the messenger's return. But it was not long before people of the district started to arrive in small groups to welcome me home and to congratulate me on my return – an event that they clearly had never expected.

In these happy reunions, the welcoming parties were

often stunned into silence as I related some of my adventures and experiences. What I had to tell seemed beyond their comprehension.

For his part, Mr Hull seemed struck by how little these visitors knew and understood of the world of the white men. This should not have been of surprise because these people had experienced little contact with traders from England. They relied on selling their elephants' teeth to local merchants as they passed by towards the River Gambia. Mr Hull noted that elephants were so plentiful in this area that the people of a small town close by had killed no less than nine last month.

Mr Hull was clearly impressed with the richness of our countryside with its many elephants, herds of cattle and goats, abundance of wildfowl including partridges and guinea fowl, and swarms of bees. On the other hand, he remarked that he was surprised local people had no notion of making wax because of their lack of contact with white men.

I felt in his diary Mr Hull might also have mentioned the warmth of the greeting and kind hospitality shown to us. The master of the house where we had been offered lodgings was exceedingly kind, mindful of our comfort and generous in his provisions. He even made a present of a cow for the benefit of our travelling party.

Friday July 4
Having decided we could wait no longer for news from Bondu, we gathered together our possessions and in the cool of the late afternoon set out for a small town called Wild, some five miles distant, where we spent the night. During this evening Mr Hull was troubled by a bout of fever, brought on, he surmised, by his exposure to the hot sun, especially during that morning when he had taken observations to find the position

of Goodery, which he calculated to be in the latitude of 14'33' north.

Saturday July 5

Today, our journey was delayed by heavy rains, but at two o'clock in the afternoon we were able to set off for the small community of Bullabuck, some fifteen miles away to the north-east. It was a hard march – especially for Mr Hull, who was still suffering from his fever – and we were pleased and relieved to reach the town without mishap at about nine o'clock in the evening.

Throughout that journey I felt that I was retracing the footsteps of my past and those of my father, family and friends. This gently contoured landscape, with its abundance of trees, shrubs, and foliage of varying colours and smells, brought memories flooding back; memories that were illuminated by the greeting of the people we encountered in the many small villages, hidden away in clearings, that we passed by. I was almost home, for Bullabuck lies just five miles from my hometown of Chambey. *Al-Hamdu lillah!* Praise be to God!

Sunday July 6

It was nine-thirty this Sunday morning – just a year after sailing away from England – that we set off on the path to Chambey. To celebrate the occasion, and to express my deep gratitude for my homecoming, I dressed myself in the white damask gown that I had brought from London, a black velvet cap and Mundingo breeches. Rather than walk, I mounted my horse for the short journey. It was not long before I glimpsed the familiar site of the dwellings that formed my home and those of my neighbours.

While the township's great drum was being sounded as a greeting, it soon became obvious that many of the houses had been weakened and damaged by weather, neglect and much worse. Chambey had suffered from fighting and strife in much the same way as many of the other ravaged communities we had visited on our journey. What I witnessed with my aching eyes was confirmed by tales recounted later by my own people. While I had been away, Bondu had disintegrated and suffered hardship in the fighting between the Sisibe and the Denianke factions. The Sisibe had restored their rule with the aid of troops from Futa Toro.

Maka Jiba, son of Bubu Malik Si, had consolidated his power over Bondu and felt emboldened to turn his fighting power on the Malinke people of the neighbouring Bambuk kingdom who remained the avowed enemies of Bondu. His successful raids brought him increased riches, which he used to buy horses and ammunition with which, in turn, he could strengthen his hold over this region.

Mr Hull, who by now was suffering the severe effects of his fever, could not disguise his disappointment with the condition of our humble dwellings. I am not sure what he was expecting; perhaps a palace or a grand house in the style of English mansions?

As we are often forced by wars or the impact of harsh weather to move about the country, our homes are simple and functional. They are small, constructed from clay with thatched roofs, and sometimes raised above the ground. By the standards of English homes, I am sure the interiors might be regarded as dark, but the lack of openings through which the sun could shine help to keep our homes cool. The buildings are dwellings, designed to protect us from the worst of the elements, not status symbols.

My travelling companion may have said little, but I learnt he recorded in his diary, 'I with much ado arrived at Mr Job's house... had I not known it to be a Mahometan Town, should have thought it to be a Hogg house.'

What an insult… to liken my home to the hut of a pig; a pig, of all animals! The pig is the dirtiest animal in all Islam. If he had exclaimed these words to my face, I would have exploded with anger at such an insult. After many weeks of accepting our hospitality I learnt that Mr Hull was complaining of unwanted bedfellows: large snakes that had slipped into his house, at least one of which he felt obliged to kill. Perhaps he was learning what it is really like to live alongside untamed nature.

Thankfully, I was oblivious to Mr Hull's true feelings on this my first day back in my hometown. My emotions were swinging from despair at seeing the sorry condition of so many familiar dwellings and euphoria at the warmth of my reception. Gleeful friends and relatives poured out of these homes, singing and dancing, to welcome us. My despair evaporated. I became ecstatic. Mounting my horse, I galloped wildly back and forth, firing guns and pistols in the air to show my happiness. *Al-Hamdu lillah!*

When I had finally calmed myself, and dismounted from my poor, exhausted horse that was barely able to stand any longer, I was able to embrace and share intimate pleasantries with my family. Once again, tears flowed from my eyes as I held close my children. I was proud to see that my sons, Abdullah, Ibrahim and Samba, had grown into strong young men, each with his own individual character but all sound in manners and spirituality. I sighed as we embraced.

And then there was dear little Fatimah, still barely five years of age; such a pretty girl who was destined to break so many hearts. She looked on me as a stranger (for, indeed, that is what I was) and yet, in my absence, she had been tutored by her mother Sadika as to my role and the depth of my love. Thanks largely to Sadika, Fatimah had developed a lively, enquiring mind. She was so full of questions. Where had I been? Why had I gone away? Why was I wearing such rich robes? I hugged her tightly, determined to make up for my absence and eager to start a proper father-daughter relationship.

I was pleased to find that both of my wives, Aisha and Sadika, were healthy and content, although I swallowed hard to restrain my emotions when I learn that Sadika, having remarried, was living with her new husband away from Bondu, having initially spent some time together in the same house that we had shared. But how could I blame her? Like everyone in Bondu, she must have assumed that given my capture and shipment to America, I would never be seen or heard from again. That was how it was.

In a sense, I had returned from the dead. I was fortunate indeed to have been allowed to make the return journey to my home, even more so given the pleasurable associations and activities that I had experienced following my enslavement and release from capture.

But as the euphoria evaporated from my senses, I again saw that all was not well in Bondu. The damage to buildings, the laying waste of crops and the disappearance of prized animals was evidence of the wars of which I had been informed in Joar back in February. At my insistence my family gave me a brief, but painful, account of what had taken place in my absence.

The remainder of that day passed as if in a whirlwind, with so many friends and dignatories visiting from neighbouring towns and villages, eager to welcome me and Mr Hull and to hear of my exploits in America and England. The astonished looks on their faces as I recounted some of my experiences would stay in my memory for the rest of my life.

Finally, that evening, as we grew weary from the exertions and excitement of the day, a messenger arrived from Phenah, eight miles south of my home, bearing a formal welcome to the country from Maka Jiba, the ruler of Bondu. Perhaps I should have felt pleased and honoured by the ruler's gesture. But looking about me at the widespread damage I experienced no elation.

At least I had returned home! It was Allah I needed to thank. I was so grateful for this miracle and for protecting me through all that had happened in recent years that I vowed that for the next month I would keep a strict fast.

Monday July 7

Today the celebrations continued, although Mr Hull was no more than an impassive onlooker, laid low from the fever and the effects of his exertions. As for me, I was flying high; overflowing with relief and happiness.

The messenger from Phenah was sent back with a message from Mr Hull explaining the purpose of his mission and promising that he himself would wait upon the king at the earliest possible moment. In Mr Hull's mind, that king – Al Iman Maka Jiba to give him his full name – was called 'Eleman Maccah'.

Tuesday July 8

I continued to renew acquaintances and intimacies with the new dawn. I was still in a joyful mood. But poor Mr Hull remained in a sorry state. Reference to the wet weather and 'nothing remarkable' were his only diary comments for this day.

Wednesday July 9

Today a group of merchants passed through on their way from the River Gambia to the other side of the River Senegal by Gallam. They brought with them a herd of many cows, and news that the French factory at Albreda had been ransacked and all its money had been carried away to Senegal.

Thursday July 10 to Sunday July 13

Four days after our arrival, I was overjoyed when we received a visit from my friend and fellow student Samba Gueladio Diegui, accompanied by two of my elder brothers. I embraced them all in turn. All of us found it hard to express in words our joy and true feelings. Each of us was longing to describe all that had happened to us in recent years, but the words would just not come. So, we contented ourselves with repeated greetings, hugs and back-slapping.

Eventually, our excitement subsided, partly through exhaustion, but also because of distressing news that I was told I needed to hear. Samba told me how he was now the exiled Siratick of Futa Toro, having been overthrown as leader of the Denianke dynasty by his younger brother Konko Bubu Musa and forced to take refuge with the ruler of Bondu in Phenah.

I had learnt much about the fighting that had taken place during my absence – the testament was to be found in the broken towns and villages we had encountered on our journey. I had also heard of Samba's plight. But now, as he stood before me, a defeated warrior, I realised the personal suffering and humiliation he had been forced to endure. It was etched on his face.

'I'm so very sorry,' I said. 'But you are a great man, a born leader, and I have no doubt you will return to rule again. Of that I am certain.'

'Thank you,' was all that Samba said in response.

We then stood together in silence and in close embrace. At that moment there seemed to be no need for spoken words. The time would come later for reminiscing, for sharing tales from our younger years and for describing our exploits and adventures.

Finally, the silence was broken.

'Brother, it is so good to see you again,' said Samba as his eyes explored my face as if for tell-tale signs of torture and hardship.

'I feared you were lost forever, for we have always been told slaves never return.'

'But I have, and I have so much to tell you how it all came about,' I replied. 'But not now... there will be plenty more days when we can explore our lives more deeply.'

Samba nodded in agreement. We both knew this was the time for embracing, for sharing tears and laughter, and for renewing the bonds of friendship that had tied us together so tightly in our early years. We were both aware that neither of us then could have imagined how our lives would have been shaped in the intervening years.

And so, we parted with a promise that we would soon meet again to continue renewing our deep friendship.

A reminder of our bonds came within a few days; first, when one of Samba's princely brothers – also in exile – called on me and then, on the eighteenth of the month, when one of Samba's sisters called. Her mission was again to welcome me home, although she did take the opportunity to try and sell Mr Hull some gold. Alas, on this occasion a trade could not be completed because Mr Hull was unable to provide in return a quantity of amber – always a coveted item in these parts.

Thankfully, given the opportunity of rest, Mr Hull grew stronger, if no more affable, as he recovered from his fever. He even took the opportunity to go on a short shooting expedition. As for me, I kept to my fast and prayers as I renewed my bonds with my family and friends. Gradually, I felt more and more comfortable as I adjusted back to my old pace of life.

Monday July 14
This morning I travelled with Mr Hull and an interpreter to

Phenah to meet with Al Iman Macca. Phenah is a sizeable town that had become probably the most important place in Bondu, the residence of leading religious and civil leaders. We arrived at about noon and as we approached Mr Hull felt it appropriate to fire a salute in greeting. The salute had a greater impact than was probably intended because one of the pistols exploded and burst, fortunately without doing undue harm.

Our discussions lasted well into the afternoon, when Al Iman Macca promised he would do all he could to help Mr Hull and the company. As a sign of his goodwill, the ruler insisted on accompanying us for part of the way to my home, even though it was raining hard and we all became thoroughly drenched.

Tuesday July 15 to Thursday July 17

Our routine these two days was punctuated by a little trading and an unexpected visit. After some haggling, I sold two rings of gold to Mr Hull. We welcomed the arrival of Al Iman Macca's brother, who had been dispatched to meet with Mr Hull as a sign of goodwill. And one of the exiled princes of Futa Toro came to Chambey specifically to see me.

Friday July 18

The ruler himself visited us on this day. Al Iman Macca paid Mr Hull a great compliment by extending an invitation to stay with him in Phenah and to go shooting for wild animals. To my surprise the invitation was not taken up but, as I was learning, Mr Hull was not much of a sociable or communicative being. That said, I did manage to persuade Mr Hull to join me on an expedition to shoot wildfowl at a favourite waterway of mine, an excursion that we would repeat on a few occasions.

With my life now taking on a semblance of my familiar past, it is an opportune moment to draw this diary to an end.

◇◇◇

Our presence in Bondu, while greeted with so much pleasure by all those around me, had not gone unnoticed further afield. As I had learnt as a child, news travels quickly in the bush of Bondu. Soon two of my elder brothers came to visit me and to question me deeply on all my adventures. Another visitor was my sister, who thoughtfully brought a present of a goat which provided a handsome feast.

To my great delight, and some surprise, my second wife, Sadika, returned, bringing with her our lovely daughter, Fatimah. She stayed for three days, during which time we all became happily reacquainted, before she left with my blessing to return to her second husband. I was content that I had been reunited with my faithful wife Aisha, on whom I had been happy to bestow gifts, including many small silver coins made into two bracelets, as a token of my love and appreciation for her loyalty.

I have no doubt that the warmth, love and excitement that I was sharing with my family during this period must have only aggravated the deep melancholy being displayed by Mr Hull. For the poor man was much troubled by malaria-type illness, marked by chills, fever and vomiting, and thus was in no mood to join me in my celebrations.

It was not long after our arrival that a messenger representing French traders arrived to greet Mr Hull and question him on his intentions. The messenger had travelled from a fort – St Joseph's – that the French had established at Maccana, on the Senegal River in the kingdom of Gallam, not that far away. The fort lies about twenty-two miles downstream the Senegal River from its junction with the Faleme River, which is but six miles distant from my home.

Mr Hull, who was still under the influence of the fever

and, in consequence, was not in a happy mood, made it plain to the messenger that if those at the fort wished to communicate with him, they should do so in a language other than French, which he could not understand. A few days later the messenger returned with a letter written only in French. It had been addressed by Monsieur de Balmauir, the Governor of Gallam, on behalf of the Compagnie des Indes, the French trading company.

As none of us could understand French, the messenger kindly explained the main points of the letter which was retained by Mr Hull and later translated.

The letter read as follows:

> 'I have learnt, Sir, that some Europeans have arrived in Bondu, and although I cannot know whether or not they can read French, I am writing on chance to offer them, in case of need, whatever help I can. The French are always ready to offer help to strangers who are in a position to receive it.
>
> 'If you can read this letter, I must beg you to reply and make known your needs. I shall do all that I can to help you. May I ask you to tell me what your purpose is in this country? If it is trade that has brought you here, you need not fear that I shall be jealous or do anything to interfere with you. If you are here by accident you can rely on the help of a Frenchman and Christian.'

I must say I considered the sentiments expressed in the letter to be most civil and welcoming.

'I know of this man,' said Mr Hull on rereading the English version of the letter. 'I believe Monsieur de Balmauir has a brother, trading in the Gambia. No doubt he thinks that I may be carrying a letter for him from his brother.'

Mr Hull immediately wrote a letter in reply. It was dated Bundo, July 28, 1735, and, for a reason known only to Mr Hull it was addressed to Monsr. Belmore (presumably because it sounded more English). It read:

'*I just received Yours of the 21St ult. But as to the Contents therein am uncapable of knowing, by reason, as I desir'd your Messenger when here before, to acquaint You that I could not read French; but as to your Linguist telling me anything You have got at your Fort is at my service, I return You my best thanks.*

'*I was sent here by the English Company's Governor and Chiefs of James Fort, with one Job, a Native of this Country, who was made a Slave about 5 Years since and afterwards carried in to England, made free and sent back into his own Country by the Royal African Company, to see that he nor his things was not abused by the Natives in the River Gambia.*

'*As to your Brother's sending You a Letter by me, is what he did not, for he did not know of my coming into those parts tho' he was in a large ship in the river Gambia when I came away.*

'*If you have got anyone with You that could write in English, should be glad you would do me the favour of letting me receive a Line or two from You.*

'*I hope You will Excuse this, being very much out of Order, so conclude, wishing you health, tho' unknown.*'

About two weeks later, on August 14, two new messengers, known in these parts as laptots – freed black slaves who were now in the service of the French – arrived with a large parcel and letter from Mr de Balmauir. It seemed that Mr de Balmauir had grown concerned about Mr Hull's state of health, especially his fever, as well as the lack of familiar comforts. Again, the letter was in French, translated as follows:

> *'I am sending you, Sir, 20 biscuits, 5 pints of brandy, 2 pints of red wine, 1 sugar loaf, 1 pint of oil, some vinegar and a few other luxuries, acting on the report of my laptots' report that you are in need of such things.*
>
> *'Unfortunately, I cannot read your letter any better than you can mine and I am distressed that you cannot know how much I should like to supply you with what you must need to survive. If the route is open and your business allows you to come here, it would give me great pleasure to welcome you.'*

I was with Mr Hull as he eagerly opened the handsome parcel. Inside he found just twenty biscuits and a bottle of brandy. Although Mr Hull had no knowledge of the French tongue, he could make out from the letter that other items seemed to have been listed.

When questioned by Mr Hull, the laptots said that while the Governor had packed many provisions, bearers could not be found to carry the goods for fear of encountering the natives of Bondu.

'I am more inclined to think that most of the provisions disappeared during the journey – probably to friends or villains,' commented Mr Hull in a confiding manner.

'Perhaps some of the goods found their way into the laptots' stomach,' I added knowingly.

Mr Hull quickly wrote a letter to be taken back to Mr de Balmauir that evening. It read:

> *'I have just received yours of the 16th ult. as likewise*

*that 20 Biscakes and bottle of Brandy for which I
return you my best thanks; But as to the Contents
of Your Letter am unsensible of, which is no small
uneasiness to me, for did I know the Contents, I then
might perhaps be capable of sending You an Answer
suitable to this which I received.*

'*I have no more to add than that I am perfectly
recover'd of the Fever which I had on me, when Your
last Messenger was here & that I return you many
thanks for these and all other favours, which you are
so kind as to bestow on, Sir, Your most obedient and
most humble Servant.*'

It was about this time, the evening of August 14 to be
precise, my community suffered the loss of four calves that had
been killed by wild cats. Such attacks on our valuable animals
have always been a threat in these wild parts and our men are
constantly on guard. But this time the herdsmen were caught
with their defences down. Early the next morning, I was joined
by a great throng of men to hunt down these beasts, but alas,
we were unsuccessful. I have no doubt they were sleeping with
bellies full, well-hidden in the undergrowth.

Throughout our time in Bondu, Mr Hull continued to
receive encouraging signals from Al Iman Macca. He was
invited to an assembly of elders on September 9 to consider
'some extraordinary affairs concerning the country's good'
and the promotion of trade. Mr Hull and I noted that the ruler
also wanted to discuss my well-being and role in any trade
agreement.

Regrettably, Mr Hull felt unable to attend the assembly. I
have no doubt he was still feeling low following his fight with
the fever, although he gave as a reason that he was now without
a horse, given that several of our animals had also suffered

from sickness in recent weeks. But I also suspect that Mr Hull may have been nervous about his reception at the assembly given the established influence of the French, as shown in the language of messages received.

So, I was asked to travel to the assembly alone. It was a great responsibility but here, in my own familiar country, I felt comfortable; far more at ease than when I was in the palaces and great country houses of England. I felt that discussions, as well as the feasting and entertainment, went well, for I was afforded courtesy and great hospitality.

On September 13 I returned to Bondu and informed Mr Hull that the assembly seemed well pleased with the Royal African Company and that the opportunity for a trading agreement was favourable. Mr Hull smiled approvingly at this news. However, his mood changed when I added that the assembly also agreed to stand by the company 'against the French or others' and that the company would be afforded all possible security and encouragement for their servants and property.

'I do not like the sound of that,' said Mr Hull, adding, 'whatever assurances the assembly might have given, it indicates the French are out to make mischief.'

'I fear you may be right,' I replied, choosing this as the most appropriate moment to pass on other intelligence I had gathered at the assembly. I was told that the French Governor at nearby Fort St Joseph had offered a reward to anyone who could deliver Mr Hull into his hands.

'I told them they were fools for not taking the money and then deceiving them without endangering you,' I assured Mr Hull.

But my companion was deeply troubled.

CHAPTER 9

Conflict and French threats

We did not need to wait long.

At about seven o'clock the next morning on September 14, we heard gunfire at either St Joseph's Fort on the Senegal River, or the nearby village of Maccana. We could only assume that French vessels had arrived. At one o'clock that same day the guns sounded again – sixteen times to be precise – a further indication of the arrival of supply boats. Mr Hull told me he was aware that a fleet of shallow draught boats, carrying provisions and trading goods, were sent up the river each year when the annual floods made the river navigable.

'I've no doubt that the great sums of money being offered for my life, or at least expulsion from this country, shows how worried they are about competition. They fear that our company could establish a factory and compete for their trade,' Mr Hull confided.

In time, in our conversations, Mr Hull reinforced his plan

to try and establish a factory in Bondu. I was regarded as a vital influence in the successful execution of this plan. But his true aim was much more ambitious.

His ambition was to cross the Faleme River into Bambuk and capture their gold trade on behalf of the company. It is hard to underestimate the riches that lie in Bambuk. The country is peppered with small mines, usually no more than five or six feet deep because the local workers are wary of earth falling in on them, especially in the rainy seasons. In many instances, there is no reason to even dig mines because it is possible to scrape the earth and use water and a panning technique to separate gold from the rock and dust.

The ideal route into Bambuk is up the Sanon Kole river, or the River of Gold as some Europeans called it. Sanon Kole flows into the Faleme only a few miles from my home in Bondu. Once in Bambuk, Mr Hull intended to travel to the gold mines in the mountains of Nettico, about 100 miles east of the Faleme, in the centre of Bambuk. Here there are particularly rich mines situated near the village of Tambacoura. Mr Hull was hoping that I would make the necessary introductions while relying on Al Iman Macca to provide the promised warriors for protection.

It seemed like a good idea. But it soon became apparent that this plan might come to nought when we received word that fierce hostilities had broken out between the neighbouring kingdoms of Bambuk and Kassan.

'I regret that compared with the quiet composure of England, this must seem like a quarrelsome country, always at war with itself,' I commented.

Mr Hull smiled at this remark. 'I am pleased you found us so at peace with ourselves,' he said. 'All I can say is you must have visited us on a good day! When it comes to feuds with our neighbours – inside and outside of England – I regret to say we too have had many battles.'

Within days we had a visit from Hamman Samba, one of the elders of Bondu, and a man from Nettico who told us that the hostilities between Bambuk and Kassan had been short-lived and settled. But this proved to be a false dawn, for ten days later we heard that the people of Kassan were again attacking their Bambuk neighbours, taking captives for the slave trade.

Mr Hull was not to be thwarted in his ambition, however, and opportunities seem to present themselves when on October 10 a man named Tommamy Yaule arrived to discuss business opportunities. He was an important trader from Furbana in Bambuk and following their discussions Mr Hull told me Bambuk people seemed to prefer trading with the English rather than the French.

'The French are not at all liked by any of the natives because they are too proud and insulting and abusive to the Blacks,' he explained.

This was encouraging news, indeed, especially as Tommamy Yaule had indicated he would be prepared to help Mr Hull visit the gold mines at Nettico. Two weeks later, after further discussions and deliberations, Mr Hull sent me to Al Iman Macca to arrange a suitable escort for us to travel to Furbana. There were plenty of pleasantries and nods of agreement but little by way of an immediate assurance of support. So, I returned home to report on this non-committal response. Further communications over the following weeks were met with worrying excuses and delays.

We were also kept abreast of the various power struggles and battles by my good friend Samba during his most welcome visits to my home. And then on October 31 he called to explain that he would be away for some time.

'I can wait no longer,' he told me. 'I am impatient to reclaim my title as the rightful ruler of Futa Toro. Wish me well, Ayuba.'

I was not surprised, because Samba was always a brave and persistent warrior who could never accept defeat. In the event, the struggle proved tougher than Samba might have expected, because it would be several more years before he achieved his ambition.

A few days after that visit, on November 4, Mr Hull and I travelled to a trading town called Kaynoura, close to the Faleme River, to see if another important trader, Slattee Cabalie, would help us travel to Furbana. This was an inauspicious and painful visit for me, because on the way I was thrown from my horse, dislocating my shoulder. Fortunately, Mr Hull knew what to do and he was able to manipulate my shoulder back into place.

We discussed trade with Slattee Cabalie and I reminisced, for I well-remembered visiting Kaynoura, and the chapel of the nearby St Pierre fort. The chapel contains many religious pictures which taught me in early life how followers of the Christian faith worshipped their idols. To me, as a follower of Islam, this seemed bewildering and totally wrong.

The next day Slattee Cabalie called on us and promised not only to take us to Furbana, but also beyond to Nettico. At last we seemed ready for departure. But then, four days later – on November 9 – a messenger arrived from the Master of Nettico himself, urging us to wait until the end of the rainy season because their feud with the people of Kassam was continuing and roads would be very dangerous, especially for a white man.

The warning was reinforced a few days later by Al Iman Macca at a meeting in Phenah, when Mr Hull was assured that Tommamy Yaule would welcome him in Furbana. Al Iman Macca said we would be accompanied on the journey, even to Nettico, but not yet; not until the fighting had ended.

Our intended visits to Furbana and Nettico seemed ill-fated, and it was not long before Mr Hull decided that we should abandon our plans... not only because of wars and diplomacy but also because of our dwindling supply of trading goods and lack of horses. Almost immediately after our arrival in Bondu, Mr Hull had sent messengers back to Yamyamacunda to collect more horses.

When messengers finally returned about three months later, on October 27, they had with them but one lone mare. All the other horses had perished on their return journey. Even this new horse was sick with gripes in the belly and had little time to live.

Almost a month later, on November 22, an important emissary from Nettico arrived to extend another invitation to travel. The visitor had brought with him a ring of gold sent by the master of Nettico as a token of his invitation and intent, especially as it seemed the fighting had finished, at least for this year. But Mr Hull declined, explaining that he was now short of money, and, lacking sufficient animals and provisions, it was impossible to travel such a distance. He would now be returning to the River Gambia and provide the Governor and Chief Factor with a report on the situation, including the invitations of assistance.

'If it is thought appropriate, I will happily return within the next two months,' he said.

Although I was becoming increasingly settled with my family and friends in familiar surroundings, I felt it imperative to accompany Mr Hull back to the Gambia. Many of my goods and gifts were still in store and I was anxious to retrieve them. I too was running out of provisions.

Before making the journey, however, I felt it prudent to move my family to Conjure, a town populated with traders some fourteen miles away, close to the Faleme River, where I had many friends who I knew would look after my loved ones if any trouble should arise. An ominous air of unrest continued to hang over these parts.

Mr Hull, who by now had lost all his horses through illness, set off by foot for Yamyamacunda on Wednesday December 3. He was anxious to make progress downriver and recorded he had little alternative but to 'trudge it'. He knew the journey would be hard and dangerous. The kingdom of Wuli was still troubled by civil war. Not wishing to be seen to be taking sides, he had taken the precaution of warning the people of Bondu not to bestow any special favours on him so as not to jeopardise friendships with the leaders of Wuli, especially Governor Endeney Seca.

After spending the night in Bullabuck, Mr Hull and his support party walked the fifteen miles to Wild where I joined them. I was fortunate in being able to travel on the back of a horse that I had purchased, so I was in a much healthier spirit. Even though Mr Hull expressed himself to be 'very much tired' from his hard morning's walk, he decided that we should continue to Goodery, another five miles' distant. There we spent the night, thankful for the rest.

To make the greatest possible haste, Mr Hull had decided that we should all travel as lightly as possible, even to the extent of foregoing water supplies. He reckoned that there would still be plenty of natural water available on our route.

You can imagine our dismay when, after a march of seven miles, we came upon the course of the Golore River, only to find it dry. Mercifully, Mr Hull acted quickly. Taking my horse, he rode at full speed to a pool he knew that was reputed to never run dry, not far away at Sittadella. The pool did contain the fresh water that he had expected, and he was able to return to us with skin bags and calabashes full of the precious liquid which, given the heat, saved us from serious illness or even death.

The store of water now became vital as we spent the next three days and two nights crossing the wilderness, although taking a different route from the one we had used before. At last we reached a well-established town in Wuli called Cohunt. This was the very place where one of the horses that had been sent to Mr Hull from the Gambia had fallen sick and died. The head of the town, Madey Setta, greeted Mr Hull and requested if he could keep as a present the bridle and saddle, carried by the stricken horse. The gift was duly given, largely I suspect, because Mr Hull was still intent on travelling lightly.

The following day, December 9, we made good progress, travelling the sixteen miles to Casong, the next town. We arrived in the late afternoon, extremely tired after our exertions. But the hero of the day was a servant to Mr Hull who, having been taken ill, had been left behind in Cohunt to recover. To the surprise of us all, the man walked into Casong at nine o'clock that evening, clearly determined not to abandon Mr Hull or to be separated from our party.

At this point in our journey, Mr Hull seemed to lose track of the days. As I came to realise sometime later, he recorded in his diary December 10 as being a Tuesday, when it should have been Wednesday. Perhaps it was his tiredness that had prompted the mistake. Or it may have been the excitement of unexpectedly being reunited with his servant. Whatever the reason, the days of the week were wrongly recorded right through to the end of the expedition.

Our next part of the journey, which followed the path of our outward route, taking us through Canophy and Sowro, was marked by the frustration of local leaders demanding gifts. We were concerned because our stock of gifts had long been exhausted. Thankfully we suffered no harm and on December 13 we arrived at Congcord where we felt that we were at least among friends.

The Governor, Endeney Seca, demonstrated his delight at our reunion by entertaining us grandly and killing a cow in our honour. But it was not all rejoicing. We were given the worrying news that the pretender to Wuli, who had been beaten by the Governor, had fled to Bondu and was on the road with a great number of local people to try to capture that country. I was sorely worried about the safety of my family and friends who I had moved to Conjure.

We rested in Congcord for three nights before setting off for Moncodaway where we arrived in the late evening. The next day, Wednesday, December 17 – but recorded as a Tuesday – we trekked the final miles into Yamyamacunda. We had been away over six months.

Mr Hull was being quite specific with his record of the journey, even if he was sparse with his description of the land through which we had traversed. He recorded in his journal that we had taken twenty-two days to travel about 185 miles from Yamyamacunda to Bondu, making an average of eight and a half miles each day. He noted that we had travelled hard while heavily loaded through the rainy season. On the return journey we had travelled an average of about fourteen miles a day, covering the journey to Yamyamacunda in just thirteen days.

Of course, Mr Hull had modern instruments and timepieces to assist with his navigation and calculations, which was just as well as he seemed to show little interest in the ways in which local people found their way from one place to another – often over very long distances – using the signs of the natural world, such as the weather, plants, smells, sounds and stars. I did not think it kindly to point out that before my capture I had travelled several times from my home to and from the Gambia, and even on one occasion had ventured far north towards Egypt, a journey of five weeks, without the aid of an instrument and using only my instinct and knowledge of the natural world.

Mr Hull also recorded in his journal, in an entry dated December 17, 1735, that it had been six months and three days since he had seen a white man. He had delivered to Mr John Cooper, the Yamyamacunda factor, 12¼ ounces of gold, most of which he had purchased but a small proportion gained through gifts. He explained he could have bought more if he had large fine coral or other goods to trade, or if he had money to compete with the French, who bought in very large quantities.

On our arrival in Yamyamacunda we soon learnt how much our journey to my homeland had troubled French officials. Almost immediately, a letter from the Council of Directors at St Louis, the capital of the French colony in the region, was delivered to Mr Richard Hull in Bondu with a copy dispatched to the English Governor at Fort James. The message could not have been clearer.

In summary, the Council expressed its surprise that the Governor of Fort James had sent us into Bondu and Bambuk to set up trading establishments in regions that had long-held commercial agreements with the French. Our declared intention was deemed to be an attempt to overturn the rights of the French.

We were therefore summoned to move away from the area and threatened with reprisals if we refused. The letter made it clear that all necessary means would be taken against 'interlopers and transgressors against the rights of the Nation'. In contrast to the hostile tone of the message, the letter was politely signed by the Council of Directors with the words 'We are perfectly The Chief Council of Directors, Your most humble and obedient Servants'.

The letter makes me think that the Governor of Fort St

Joseph really was serious when he had warned me of the possible kidnapping or assassination of Thomas Hull. From our discussions in Yamyamacunda, it was abundantly clear that the relations between the English and French trading operations were severely strained. Add to this the strife that was continuing between various tribal factions. It appeared that the whole nation was involved in disputes.

I did not feel it was my place to broadcast this state of unrest, however. So, when I sent a letter to England a few weeks later, I concentrated on my personal happiness and pleasantries. The letter was addressed to Jacob Smith, an acquaintance of Joseph Ames, the antiquary, whom I had befriended during my stay in London. Mr Smith was the writing master at the distinguished St Paul's School.

In setting down this letter, let me openly admit that I had great and welcome assistance of company men in expressing my thoughts in the English tongue.

YANIMEROW IN THE RIVER GAMBIA
JAN: 27th 1736
'Sir. This is to acquaint you of my safe arrival at and return here from Bundo, being conducted safe and used with great Civility all the Way, which was owing to the respect and regard all the Natives in every part have for the Company and by being conducted by one white Man only which was the Governor's Nephew on the Company's behalf, which made no little noise and was of much service to me. One of my Wives had got another husband in my Room and the other gave me over. My father died soon after my Misfortune of being seized and sold for a Slave, but my Children are all well. My redemption was so remarkable and surprising that my Messengers and Letters sent on my

behalf on my first arrival here were not Credited, but how elevated and amazed they were at my Arrival I must leave you to guess at as being inexpressible, as is likewise the Raptures and pleasure I enjoy'd. Floods of Tears burst their way and some little time afterward we recover'd so as to have some discourse, and in time I acquainted them and all the Country how I had been redeem'd and Conducted by the Company from such distant parts as are beyond their Capacity to conceive, from Maryland to England, from thence to Gambia's Fort, and from thence conducted to my very house, the Favours done me by the Queen, Duke of Montague and other Generous persons, I likewise acquainted them of, and all with me praised God for such his providence and Goodness, and as a more publick acknowledgment thereof I kept from arrival a Months Fast. I should think my self very happy in your Company in these parts if your Inclination continues to come in the Company's service.

I am, Sir, Your obliged and most humble servant
JOB THE SON OF SOLOMON
of the nation (or tribe) of Jalot.

Meanwhile, the French Council of Directors at St Louis was still smarting at our journey into my country, prompting a threatening letter to the Governor at Fort James on February 3, 1736, with a copy sent to Mr Hull in Bondu, charging us with trespassing. They were convinced it was our intent to establish a factory in Bondu. An English translation shows the implied threat carried in this letter:

'We believe that you have overlooked the fact that it [the proposed factory] is situated on the River Faleme, *which is part of the Senegal, on whose banks we have long had a fort and have now a market for trading in supplies. We have in neighbouring Bambuk, two small forts and our trade extends into both it and Bondou, which are dependencies of Galam and Futa Toro respectively. As we were in those regions before you we definitely cannot allow you to set yourselves up in territory to which we have the exclusive commercial rights. We are counting upon you recalling your agent (that is Mr Hull), now that we have made the position clear.'*

It was evident that there were worrying tensions between the French and English traders, not helped by the time it took to receive and reply to the letters that passed back and forth. Many of the issues concerned who held the trading rights in certain kingdoms, although I also heard there were disagreements over the prices that were being offered for slaves. An agreement existed between the French and English trading companies that the French Albreda trading post and Fort James, both on the lower reaches of the Gambia, would offer the same price for slaves which, at this time, stood at forty bars. But it seemed the French were offering fifty bars, the going rate for slaves upriver at Joar.

When, in November, Mr Hull decided to leave Bondu and return to the River Gambia, he gave an undertaking that if possible, he would return within a few months to continue to Bambuk and the gold mines. Encouraged by the Governor, he now began making arrangements for his immediate departure and I felt it only right that once again I should offer my services and accompany him. But first, I too had business to attend to. A great many of my possessions that I had brought from England were still in storage. Now that I had been reunited with my family and close friends, I was anxious to send on my goods, including so many treasured gifts, to Bondu.

Given the tribal hostilities that still existed in the lands between the Gambia and Bondu, and the likelihood that my goods would be stolen or bartered for safe passage I felt obliged to adopt what might seem an unconventional approach to this transportation problem. I called on the French to help me.

In Yamyamacunda I knew several officers in the Royal African Company who, personally, were on good terms with French traders. With their help, I arranged for a large part of my consignment to be carried on a French sloop from the Gambia to the French fort of St Joseph's in Galam, which was very close to my home in Bondu. The ship would accomplish this by sailing from the Gambia, up the coast and into the River Senegal.

As I was not wholly confident that this arrangement would be successful, I took the precaution of storing the remainder of my goods in the English factory at Yamyamacunda, where I was sure my property would remain secure.

Thomas Hull, meanwhile, was making arrangement for our second expedition, this time to Bambuk and into the gold country. His demeanour indicated he was completely unaware of the consternation being expressed in London over the diary of our first expedition that had been dispatched to African House.

The diary had been read with interest and some dismay, not so much because of what had been included in the account of our journey, but more for what had not been written. The Duke of Montagu who, through his kindness had shown so much interest in my exploits and progress, asked if he could see the diary. But as was explained in a return letter from the company to Richard Hill, '…we readily complied, but were obliged to order the best excuse to be made for the brevity and other defects of that diary.'

The tone of the letter then became more explicit. It said the company was concerned to see the diary was:

'...*barren of the useful observations and remarks that might undoubtedly have been made by Mr Thomas Hull during the long time of his residing there, but we must impute that defect to his youth and inexperience. We observe you have sent him on another progress to Bambouk and Nettico; and, as we doubt not but you have given him proper and full instructions for his conduct therein, we hope his diary of that progress will give us more satisfaction; and according as he behaves, we shall be glad to give him encouragement.*'

In the event, our second journey undertaken in the early months of 1736, turned out to be much more straightforward than our previous expedition. I put this down to greater preparedness – we had more animals and bearers to assist us this time – and easier travelling conditions, this being the dry season. We were also accompanied by one of the company's soldiers, John Kenn, who not only provided greater company and conversation but also an increased level of security in the event of any hostilities we might encounter along the way. Fortunately, our journey was uneventful and the expedition largely successful.

We identified the forests where Gum Arabic grows and were pleased to find traders willing to assist in sending this valuable product to England. I knew from my own time in England that this would be greatly appreciated, as at this time the French were responsible for supplying most of the gum.

We then moved further up country to the mountains where gold dust is washed down. Here we were heartened by new trading opportunities. We discussed how men, properly equipped and skilled in mining techniques and the separation of gold from ore, could greatly increase the export of this valuable commodity which could be moved by means of specially built flat-bottomed boats, capable of navigating the streams and rivers. If we could establish such an operation, the company would no longer be reliant on the much less valuable gold dust trade.

Our return from the expedition found us in buoyant mood. Although we had come across many instances where fighting and destruction had occurred, we had avoided encountering trouble ourselves. Most importantly, we had achieved our aim of establishing the basis for new gold and gum trading activity. I was told that my local knowledge and connections had greatly helped this venture and in return I again pledged that I would use the utmost of my power to support the company in further trading exploits in the future.

On our return I set down an account of our exploits in a letter to Sir Hans Sloane. This was dispatched on the next ship from the Gambia. The communication must have pleased Sir Hans, because he immediately communicated its contents to the Royal Society. The Gentleman's Magazine reported this communication in its issue of November 1736. The item opened with the words, 'Sir Hans Sloane communicated to the Royal Society a Letter from Job the African, whom Mr Oglethorpe released from Slavery, and the African Company sent home to his own Country about Twelve Months ago. In this Letter he very gratefully acknowledges the Favours he receiv'd in England.' The report continued:

'...in answer to some Things desir'd of him when here, says he has been in the Country where the Gum Arabick grows, (which at present we get chiefly from the French settlements) and can assist the English in

that Trade: That he has been up the Country as far as the Mountains from whence the Gold Dust is wash'd down, and that if the English would build flat bottom'd boats to go up the rivers, and send persons well skilled in separating the Gold from the Oar (with which they may soon, and with ease, load their boats) they might gain vastly more than at present they do by the Dust Trade; adding, that he should always be ready to use the utmost of his power, which is very considerable in that country, to support them therein.'

I was interested to learn later that the article about my letter was reprinted across the water in The Virginia Gazette. This time, in its edition of February 4, 1737, the American newspaper's publisher, William Parks saw fit to add his own comment:

'A Piece of News no doubt at this Time of Day very agreeable to our English Merchants, among whom there are not wanting Gentlemen of Spirits equally brave with any of their Ancestors, who are as ready, at the Hazard of their Fortunes, under proper Encouragement, to support amd increase our Trade as any of our neighbouring Nations can be to check and diminish it; our darling Trade, which has been acquir'd and establish'd at the Expence of so many Millions of Treasure, and Deluges of inestimable British Blood!'

It is a pity that Mr Parks had not seen fit to point out that it was not only British blood that was being spilled in the trading activities conducted in my homeland. I was now so much more worldly-wise. I had seen for myself the great suffering experienced by the vast number of captives as they were shipped and forced to toil in the most horrible of conditions as part of this 'darling Trade'.

I was fortunate. I had escaped. I had been shown great kindness and provided with many privileges. Even so, my contentment and feeling of well-being were to be shortlived.

CHAPTER 10

The sweet air of freedom

◇◇◇

Soon, I began to hear reports that a French sloop heading for the Senegal River had been wrecked off Portodally, on the African coast just north of the entrance to the River Gambia. It was rumoured that this was the vessel carrying my goods to St Joseph's. I decided to set off immediately for this French fort to check whether there was any truth in this rumour. I had few qualms about making this overland journey. I knew the route and terrain – I had travelled that way many times in my younger days – and I had every confidence that my knowledge of habitations and the various people I would encounter would serve me well. And, indeed, it did. I arrived safely on June 6, 1736.

To my horror, as I walked into St Joseph's Fort expecting at least a polite greeting, I was arrested and clapped in irons. The officers were under instruction not only to chase Mr Hull out of the country (confirming previous threats that I had heard) but also to capture me – 'the Negro Job'. I was humiliated and taunted by my captors. They told me I was a slave again and quite likely I would be sent to Louisiana or the West Indies.

As I lay in the barren cell of this run-down fort, I was consumed with recalling my previous experience of enslavement: the horrible passage in cramped, painful conditions of a slave ship; the beatings and starvation rations of putrid food; the indignities of dockside selection by potential masters viewing us like pieces of meat; and then the unending back-breaking labour in the fields of plantations. The nightmares were far worse than before, for now I knew what I might expect.

Little did I know how much my well-being was being considered by men of influence in the opposing trading organisations of the English and French.

The French India Company had become extremely concerned about the trading aspirations of the English company, especially given the exploits of Mr Hull, with my assistance, in Bondu and beyond. The officers of the French company, based in St Louis, exaggerated the strength of our expeditions, reporting to their superiors in Paris on June 15, 1736 that our English delegation of about sixteen people had returned from our travels in December with an escort of fifty men provided by the people of Bondu. It was claimed that we would be returning immediately with horses and asses laden with trading goods and as a result officers at St Joseph's were under instructions to chase me out of Bondu and arrest me.

Back in England, news was being received about the general situation and my plight in particular. I had sent letters through the good offices of Mr Moore to the company, the Duke of Montagu and the Earl of Pembroke. Much later replies from all these recipients were finally delivered into my hands.

The Duke and the Earl of Pembroke responded jointly

to my messages of goodwill. In a letter dated April 26, 1736, these two noblemen thanked me for the prayers of myself and fellow Muslims by responding in pious tones.

'God Almighty is Great,' they wrote. 'He is the Common Father of us all, we all worship Him, tho' in differing Form, and He hears the prayers of all who with a sincere heart call upon Him, and endeavour to follow that Universal law He has given to all mankind.'

They also expressed both their sorrow regarding the death of my father and sincere concern at news they had learnt from elsewhere concerning the loss of my goods because of the French shipwreck. They prayed that God would eventually give me 'all those Blessings and Comforts to which as a good man you are justly entitled'.

This letter, while written in ignorance of my capture, did contain some positive news, however. It said that Thomas Bluett had returned to Maryland with instructions from Mr Moore and James Oglethorpe to locate my servant and interpreter Lamine Ndiaye and procure his liberty. I was so relieved to read these words, although naturally anxious about my friend's health and condition when found... if, indeed, he could be successfully located.

After imparting this encouraging news, the noble lords informed me they had passed on my regards to their Majesties and closed by expressing they were my 'sincere friends'.

I would reread that letter many times, for it contained words of so much consideration and kindness. The sincerity shone through. Indeed, the Duke acted by pressing the Royal African Company to make strict inquiries as to how I had lost such a rich cargo of possessions that had been so carefully assembled.

The Court of Assistants, prompted by this demand, wrote to the Governor at Fort James and reprimanded him for his slackness in looking after my interest, especially as I was expected to support their trading interests in Bondu and beyond. The letter must have made for some uncomfortable reading, given the strength of its admonishment. It said that given my likely support in trading interests *The Gentleman's Magazine* reported this communication in its issue of November 1736:

'...*we might much more have expected from him had you taken Care to follow our directions and to have sent all his things as farr up the River Gambia as you could with safety and there lodged them till he could have had an Opportunity of taking them away by degrees, and indeed considering the long tedious and dangerous Navigation of the Senegal and the Rival-ship in Trade which you well know subsists between the French and us we are greatly at a loss to guess what could induce you to trust any of them in such hands, or to send them by such a round about way to him, for had Job himself desired to have had them sent this way, you ought, if you had considered the matter rightly, to have opposed it as knowing that if they were they would never be delivered to him, which it seems proves to be the Case, it being now given out, as Job himself informs us that they were lost between Gambia and Senegal, but as Job seems to question the truth of this Report we do therefore earnestly recommend it to you to make the strictest and most particular Enquiry you possibly can into this Affair, and for your own Justification as well as for the Satisfaction of Job's Friends here to acquaint us with the result thereof by the first Opportunity.*'

Meanwhile, the French were preoccupied with a damaging trading dispute of their own. They found themselves embattled in a quarrel with Tonca Tuabo, king of one of Galam's regions north-east of Bondu, regarding the payment of disputed customs. The dispute escalated to fighting, with the Tonca's men repeatedly attacking the fort. The French were forced to use the guns of St Joseph's fort for protection.

I find it hard to describe the experience of being shackled and helpless in an already crumbling fort with a gunfire all around me. The noise was deafening. I admit to being petrified that the walls of my cell would crash in on top of me. There was pandemonium, hunger, thirst and desertions as many workers in the fort fled for their lives. Thankfully the onslaught subsided, and a battered St Joseph's returned to an uneasy peace.

On November 6, 1736 Monsieur Claude St Adon, the Governor of St Joseph's who had replaced Monsieur de Balmauir, appealed to his Council at St Louis. He told them the fort was in ruins, the garrison was short of food, the firewood had all been used, the laptots had deserted and there was now a complete lack of trade. Even though the customs demanded by Tonca Tuabo had been paid, the local people were still refusing to be pacified. Traders in the area were demonstrating their support for me by rerouting their caravans away from the Senegal River to the Gambia.

There was a very good reason for this unrest. The uprising was continuing because I was being held as a captive!

Monsieur St Adon was facing a dilemma. He wrote that should the Council insist on me being sent down to them at St Louis, it would be impossible to guarantee my safety.

Less than a month later – on December 2 – Monsieur St Adon wrote again explaining the situation had become even worse. Muslim religious leaders, namely Marabouts, from the surrounding region including Bondu and the trading town of Dramanet, near the gold mines of Nettico, had become so incensed with my continued captivity they had vowed not to trade with the French until I had been set free. It was plain that this was no idle threat.

'I saw with regret that their zeal was not at all simulated, that such a scruple was really enjoined by their religion, and that the slave merchants were consequently diverting their trade to the Gambia,' wrote Monsieur St Adon.

Although I was suffering unwarranted privations, I took some pleasure and comfort in the knowledge that even in my captured state I seem to be assisting the trading ambitions of the English company.

While urging his superiors' consent to set me free, Monsieur St Adon did what he could to quell the rebellion. First, he made every effort to make me as comfortable as possible. Then, under the implicit threat of possible death, he forced me to draft a letter in Arabic, declaring to everyone that I was living in my friend's house of my own free will and was content to support any merchant who wanted to trade with the French. He even sent my priestly gown round all the Marabouts, a formality deemed necessary to reinforce my message of free trade. All the while, Monsieur St Adon maintained – cynically – that this was all for the good of the country and for my benefit. It was nothing of the sort. It was just a desperate measure of the French to revive relations with local traders in readiness for the coming trading season.

By all accounts the French governors at St Louis were furious with the way my arrest had inflamed local sentiment. Not only were they being confronted by the Tonca of Tuabo and the Marabouts, but they were also engaged in a bitter feud with the ruler of Futa Toro, Siratick Konko Bubu Musa, whose kingdom straddled the River Senegal. In September 1736, a French vessel carrying the annual tribute to the Siratick was attacked at Guiol by Konko Bubu Musa, who killed all the

Frenchmen on board, captured or killed the black crew, and pillaged all the goods and ship's furnishings.

The French took immediate steps to depose Siratick Konko, for they considered that communications and trading activities had been put in jeopardy by this attack. Worse still, the prestige of the French had been undermined. A large reward was put on Siratick Konko's head. They also tried to bribe neighbouring rulers and warriors to join them in dealing with the Siratick.

There was one person above all others who the French felt might help them in this mission. This was Samba Gueladio Diegui, the deposed Siratick and my very good friend. And so it was that on March 5, 1737 Monsieur St Adon and 'King Samba' agreed a 'sincere and lasting' alliance. The treaty was signed at Fort St Joseph.

The French company agreed to support Samba and help raise him to the Futa Toro throne. A messenger would be sent to the commander of the Ormans, the Moroccan troops, seeking their cooperation. A reward would be paid for Siratick Konko's head delivered to St Joseph's.

Monsieur St Adon promised to support Samba by providing him with ammunition – specifically rifles, powder and bullets – as well as the construction of a fort, armed with bastions and cannons, near Guiol. This fort would act as a defensive shield against competitors as well as the 'insatiable greed' of the Ormans. Samba would thus be assured of the peaceful possession of Futo Toro for him and his children.

For his part, Samba pledged to recognise the 'goodness' of the French by swearing a union and 'perfect intelligence' with its trading company. He also promised to deliver to Monsieur St Adon all those who had been involved in the massacre of white people in Futa Toro. Furthermore, to reimburse the French for the expenses incurred through this treaty, Samba promised to deliver fifty captives, slaves aged from fifteen to twenty-five years.

While the French trading company must have been pleased to have secured the enthusiastic support of my friend, the putative King Samba, I was humbled, learning that its governors felt I too should be brought back on side as quickly as possible.

The governors sent messages to Monsieur St Adon telling him that officers in Galam should either have sent me directly to St Louis before news of my capture had become known or I should have been released at the first sign of unrest. Fortunately, Monsieur St Adon had already realised that I should be let go and as a precursor to my release I was freed from bondage and treated as a guest, just as the Marabouts had been informed.

By this time, news of my capture at the hands of the French had reached London, probably by means of a message transmitted by one of the company's agents in Bondu or Bambuk. The Duke of Montagu was particularly perturbed, asking to be kept informed of my plight.

First, he was advised by the company that there were 'great hopes' the reports of my capture were untrue. Later, when my capture was confirmed, he was assured that steps had already been taken to secure my release. Charles Orfeur, who had been appointed Governor following the sudden death of Richard Hull, had already written to the French authorities at their regional trading post in Gorée, offering to ransom me and declaring that King George II, no less, would want me freed and returned from the French West Indies, or wherever I might be taken.

Unwittingly, it seems, I had become the centre of a diplomatic incident at the highest international level. By the time the Council of Directors at St Louis reported the correspondence back to Paris in August 1737, it was able to advise the response to Charles Orfeur was facile – simple. I had already been released.

My freedom had been given quietly and without fuss earlier that summer. By then, Monsieur St Adon and I had established a surprisingly civil, if not particularly warm, relationship given all that had gone before. I even took it upon myself to help my erstwhile captor obtain a quantity of fine black linen and some lustrous carnelian gemstones, both of which were valuable articles of trade. But at that time, I was thinking little of trading activities. I just wanted to make the short journey back to my home, to again taste the sweet air of freedom, and to quietly re-establish my pious, happy life among my family and friends.

It was on my return to my home country of Bondu that I received more disturbing news. Not only had I lost so many of my possessions in the wreckage of the French sloop, but the remainder of my goods, stored at the English company's factory at Yamyamacunda, had also been lost in a fire that badly damaged the trading post on August 9, 1736.

I was familiar with this factory, which had been erected only a few years earlier in 1733. The new factory had been built on raised land, some fifty yards from the Gambia River, after the previous building had been devastated by flood waters during the summer of that year. This new trading post was well-designed and constructed to provide an entrance porch, apartments, a large hall, some forty feet long, a kitchen, storage rooms, two lodging rooms, a well, and storage houses for salt and corn. The main building was protected by a roof of straw tied in small bundles and lashed together in a very secure fashion. The whole site was surrounded by a strong fence and marked by a large flag flying from a tall post.

I know that Mr Moore was particularly proud of the new Yamyamacunda construction for he recorded that the factory had been built by servants alone, with no hired help, and 'without any Iron-work, Trowells, Squares, or Carpenters Rules, and with the smallest Expence to the Company'.

Having seen the implements used by specialist construction workers in England, I can understand why Mr Moore might have been impressed. I can only say that I did not share his implied surprise, for the skills and enterprise of our people, passed down through generations, have always been evident in these lands.

However well the factory had been constructed, it afforded no protection from the ravages of fire of 1736. It appeared that with the loss of this factory and my possessions, fate itself had ordained that all tangible reminders of my time in England should be erased.

While I was disappointed to lose these goods that had been given with so much kindness and generosity – especially the tools and implements that I was keen to demonstrate to family and friends – I cannot say I was distraught. Within the Fulani tradition, the boastful display of wealth has always been frowned upon.

And so it was that my life returned more to the rhythm and activities that were familiar to me in my youth and would have accompanied my dear father throughout his time on earth. I took satisfaction from overseeing the tending to animals and the growing of crops. I was also pleased to follow my father in an Islamic leadership role within my community; preaching and teaching. And I continued to trade, mostly on behalf of my family and neighbours in Bondu, but also – from time to time – in association with the company. It was during these trading missions I received various messages from England.

On one of these occasions I made the acquaintance of a most interesting addition to the company's officers, an Armenian gentleman named Melchior de Jaspas who had the distinction of being able to read and speak Arabic. It transpired that he had translated some of the most recent letters that I had sent to England.

Mr de Jaspas, who was appointed as assistant to the company's chief merchants, arrived in Gambia on the packet *Guinea* in August 1737, accompanied by a Persian boy slave called Joseph and a secretary, John Buchanan, a Scottish gentleman who sadly died a few days after his arrival. Mr Buchanan had succumbed to an illness that seemed to be sweeping James Island. Tragically, another new arrival, a new trader named James Anderson who had planned to travel with Mr de Jaspas, also died within days of stepping off his ship.

The company had high hopes for the success of Mr de Jaspas as evidenced by the compliments recorded in its great ledgers. The man had been recommended to the company as a 'very honest and able person'. Subsequently he was praised for his good character, behaviour and management of the company's affairs. He could not only understand the Arabic spoken in my country but he was also thought capable of learning any other language in a short time. Mr de Jaspas was said to be keen to travel and make new discoveries in the inland parts of Africa. As a result, the company hoped he would provide a 'great service' in maintaining the considerable trade between its factories and Bondu but would expand trading links with other areas, especially those rich in gold.

Mr de Jaspas carried with him a letter addressed to me at 'Boonda in Africa'. It was sent by the company's Court of Assistants, dated May 19, 1737 and said, somewhat formally:

> '*Sir*
> '1. *It was with much satisfaction and pleasure that we received your two Letters to us dated the 19th and 23rd days of July 1736 whereby we were informed of your*

safe arrival at Boonda after having undergone so many Difficulties and Misfortunes which were however in the latter part of your Absence from your Native Country attended with Blessings and good Success, towards promoting the last of which we have contributed as much as possible, and shall continue to do so.

'2. We are concerned that you lost so many of your things and wish you had not desired them to be sent in the French Sloop by way of Senegal, but rather left them in the Care of our Chief Merchants at James Fort till they could have found means to send them safe to you up the River Gambia. That French Sloop as we are informed was lost by stress of Weather on the Shore of Portodally, but if she had not been so lost we should have been doubtful of the French conveying and delivering your things safe, by the Way of the River Senegal. Our Chief Merchants at James Fort Gambia inform us that some of your things were destroyed by the fire that burnt down our Factory at Yamyamacunda, and we have ordered them to make a Strict Enquiry into the Truth of the Loss of those which were in the French Sloop.

'3. We have delivered the Compliment which you recommended to us in your Letters to the Several persons.

'4. We are pleased with the other part of the Contents of your Letters related to the Carrying on a Correspondence, as also a trade in your Country and the better to answer both those purposes have entertained Mr Melchior de Jaspas the Bearer of this Letter as Assistant to be employed by our Chief Merchants,

and we believe you will soon find him to be a very good and a very understanding Man, and therefore we recommend him to your favour and friendship. We have ordered him to make your King a present, and another present to you of which we desire your Acceptance as a token of the Respect and Friendship we bear you. We desire that we may constantly hear from you, we wish you good health, long Life and all other Blessings that it may please God to bestow on you.'

The letter was written in English and I was grateful to Mr de Jaspas for assisting my comprehension. It was signed by 'Your Loving Friends': Sir Bibye Lake, the Sub Governor, Charles Hayes, Deputy Governor and all the other members of the Court of Assistants.

I was deeply touched and extremely well pleased.

But that was not to be the end of my joy. In the following year, I was – at last – reunited with my faithful servant Lamine Ndiaye who had also achieved the seemingly impossible: returning to his homeland from slavery in Maryland. And again, it was Mr Bluett and the Duke of Montagu who had done so much to make it possible.

I had written a letter to His Grace asking him to help try and locate Lamine and let me have any news, even if my friend had died. At the same time, I asked him to convey greetings to 'my dear friends', including the King and Queen, and informed him that I included him in my prayers. Finally, I appealed to him to 'let me know how you are'.

Mr Bluett had returned to Maryland back in 1735 and, through his extensive contacts, managed to locate Lamine who had been forced to endure the hardship of captivity for so long. Lamine had been located on a plantation in Pokomoke, in Maryland's Somerset County.

I was not surprised to learn that my friend had proved himself to be a reliable worker, an 'excellent slave', as he was described. Unfortunately, this proved to be a challenge for those seeking his release. Mr Bluett reported to His Grace that he feared it would make it harder for him to obtain Lamine, especially as he had promised 'to buy him as cheap as possible'. Mr Bluett added that he had not dared mention the Duke's involvement in the affair, 'lest that should enhance the price' even more.

Mr Denton, who had sold Lamine and me to plantation owners was contacted to assist in the transaction and a deal was finally agreed through the Provincial Court, thanks to the involvement of Michael Howard, Surveyor General of the Eastern Shore; Col Levin Gale, a member of the Council of Maryland and even Lord Baltimore, Governor of Maryland. It was settled that Lamine would be replaced with another slave of similar suitability.

The transaction had once again demonstrated how fortunate Lamine and I were to have been befriended and assisted by such an influential attorney; one so well-acquainted with the Maryland's decision makers and their court system as Mr Bluett.

And I shall be eternally grateful that the kind-hearted Duke of Montagu provided the funds to buy Lamine's freedom and take him to London. Like me, Lamine was given lodgings and looked after by the Royal African Company from the time of his arrival, late in 1737, to his departure for Gambia on a man-of-war in February 1738.

Richard Spence, the Company Secretary, sent a letter to Charles Orfeur and the other chief agents at Fort James bearing instructions on how Lamine Ndiaye was to be treated:

'The bearer, Lahamin Joy, a black Man, is the Person who was taken and sold with Job and carried with

him to Maryland; and by the great goodness of His Grace the Duke of Montague, he being redeemed from his Slavery and brought from thence hither; he now takes his passage for your Place in the [blank] Man of War, Capt. [blank] in order to return to Job and his own Country, and His Grace having desired that he may be recommended from the Company to you; I am therefore directed particularly to recommend it to you, upon his arrival at James Fort to receive and entertain him at the Company's Expense and treat him kindly, until you can send him up, either with Mr De Jaspas, if he be not gone up the Country, or by the first convenient opportunity that may offer, and likewise to give him the best advice and assistance you can for that purpose. I am further to acquaint you that the Company will write to you in favour of this Man by their own ship the Happy Deliverance which will very soon be dispatched from hence for Gambia.'

You can imagine the joy I felt when a messenger delivered the news of Lamine's arrival at Fort James. I was anxious to return with the messenger but was advised that I should remain and prepare an appropriate welcome in Bondu. This I did, assembling all manner of friends and family, for the time that Lamine would return, accompanied by company representatives.

We prayed and thanked God for the freedom bestowed on this friend and faithful servant who, against all odds, had returned from slavery in America. Lamine and I shared quiet tear-filled moments together as we recalled our induced hardships. We needed no words to demonstrate our bonds were strong for we had become more like brothers.

Gradually our mood lightened, and we felt able to share in

the general celebrations. There was much music, dancing and feasting to accompany our joy in being reunited.

And so, in these happier circumstances, life returned more to normality. My association with the company continued, either as an advisor and guide, on one occasion in company with Mr de Jaspas, or as a trader on behalf of my family and community.

On one of these trading ventures, in 1740, I visited Fort James, where I drew courage to suggest I might be invited back to London to renew acquaintances with the Duke of Montagu, Sir Hans Sloane and all my other friends both inside and outside of the company, who had made me feel so welcome in the past. I was pleased that Mr Orfeur agreed to forward my request to the Court of Assistants in London, because I was also keen to use my improved English to learn more about the ways of England and perhaps assemble a collection of tools and instruments to replace some of those that I had lost in the two tragic accidents.

Mr Orfeur presented me with the company's present of twenty-five bars and urged me to return to my country together with Mr de Jaspas and wait for a response from London.

Unfortunately, the reply, dated March 26, 1741, was negative. The answering letter from the Court to Mr Orfeur and his other Chief Agents, Hugh Hamilton and Samuel Turner, said:

'You did very well in taking the opportunity to send Job up again to his own Country with Mr Jaspas, and we approve of your treating Job kindly while at the Fort, and of the Present of 25 Bars you made him on his going away; and if he should apply to you to come to England again, we would have you by all means discourage the same: But as to the 2 slaves and the *several other things said to belong to him as mentioned in your 16th Paragraph, if you are satisfied those things were applied to the Company's use you may give Job credit for them, and also for the value of the two Slaves, in case (as Job asserts) he did deliver them to the Company's Factor Mr Roots.'*

I was disappointed at not being able to return to London, but I still had some commercial matters to settle with the company. Early on my return to the Bondu I had pledged a valuable watch, against the purchase of two slaves. This was the very watch that had been presented to me so charmingly by Her Majesty the Queen herself. When this watch was lost in the fire at the Yamyamacunda factory, I felt I had every right to claim its value from the company.

Unfortunately, the company in London took a different view, writing on October 11, 1744 it had no obligation to reimburse the value of the watch. The letter added that they were 'already sufferers to the amount of those slaves and further he can be no loser, since the 2 slaves were at least the full of his said watch'.

By this time the company had much reduced its interest in slaves anyway, preferring to concentrate on its trading of elephants' teeth and gold, although it was not averse to using independent traders – and their slaves – to supply them with these valuable commodities. I was one of those who, from time to time, continued to assist the English traders, guiding them to the gold deposits in the Galam region, and the trees and shrubs providing gum Arabic on the northern savanna. I also used the facilities of the company to carry – and receive – the occasional correspondence with my former distinguished friends.

Perhaps inevitably, these contacts became more irregular

as my contacts dwindled through retirements, illness and, I am sad to relate, even death during feuds that continued to trouble us all in my part of the world. It was not only the Sisibe and Denianke factions that were locked in continuing friction. From way before my birth, marauding armies under the control of Morocco rulers had raided Bondu to capture men for their slave army. These raids were continuing into the 1740s, adding to the unrest and strife of my people.

But in terms of government, the Sisibe under Maka Jiba now had firm control of Bondu and were flexing their muscles, a situation that was of concern to Sule Ndiaye, the Denianke ruler in Futa Toro. He could see how the Sisibe influence over Bondu and the Upper Senegal region in general was being strengthened.

Sule Ndiaye thus put down a marker and challenged Maka Jiba by demanding a tribute. He did so in a remarkable way, by writing a letter as 'the glorious, powerful and formidable', ruler of all Futa:

> '...he who was created in order to be destined for eternal life in order to be happy here below, and in order to be destined for eternal life in the other world... he who is so kind and charitable to his friends as well as being dreadful, redoubtable and implacable towards his enemies, to his lowly and faithful servant Maka-Jiba... greetings.'

The letter then set down his demands: gold 'in large supply', an all-white Arabian horse in Maka Jiba's possession and one of Maka Jiba's wives. Sule Ndiaye was also specific in this respect, adding a threat and insult for good measure:

> 'I have learned that, among your wives, you have

one who knows how to prepare couscous well; it will be necessary to send her to me also so that she can prepare my food. All of this is to be done immediately, otherwise you will force me to come to Bondu.

'I think that you would like to avoid my coming, because if I come to Bondu there will only be death and ruin, and I swear to smash over your head the lone calabash that your parents left to you in your inheritance, which you still use in obtaining alms from the hands of others, as they themselves obtained alms when you were alive.'

Maka Jiba refused the demands and convened a war council to prepare for an attack, which soon came. The Denianke army did enter Bondu in an attempt to wrest back control. After some early successes they were eventually overwhelmed and were forced to retreat back to Futa Toro.

Thankfully, the rulers of each dynasty eventually saw sense, realising that Bondu, a country with so much potential that they each cherished, was being ruined by these continuing feuds. Consequently, the Sisibe ruler signed a peace treaty, recognising the independence of Bondu. Sadly, that peace came too late to save the lives of my fellow countrymen or prevent the enslavement of so many people captured in all the fighting.

Conflicts were not only confined to Bondu. On a much grander scale – and of even more significance to our trading activities – war broke out between Britain and France in 1743, although the rival trading companies of the two nations did try unsuccessfully to create an area of neutrality in Africa. Naval vessels and merchant ships travelled in convoys to maintain trading activities. But the war footing was dramatically demonstrated when, in June 1745, the British sent a long boat and a barge carrying one hundred men to destroy the French factory at Albreda in the kingdom of Barrah, to the north of James Island.

All this took on a personal note when I found that both Charles Orfeur and Mr de Jaspas had been among those murdered by the 'natives' of Barrah in 1745. I can only assume this was a reprisal for perceived injustices felt by those in and around Albreda.

It was the death, several years earlier, of a very special friend that struck me the hardest and left me in the deepest pit of despair. According to stories that were told, Samba Gueladio Diegui was murdered. This great man and leader, with whom I had shared so many happy times, especially in our childhood, was poisoned by a treacherous wife who had been corrupted by his enemies during his time in Bondu while in exile from Futa Toro.

Even in death, it seems, Samba displayed great bravery. According to stories told by his followers he was aware of his fate, telling his wife:

> 'You put poison in my food, and this after the conversation we had the other day. I know this food will kill me. Never shall it be said that I was afraid of death. Only before dishonour do I draw back. Never do I retreat before death.'

No-one can dispute that Samba was fearless and a great warrior. It is said that during his life he led his well-armed fighters in no less than forty-five battles, spurred on by the sound of blood drums and war songs. No-one can deny he was a leader.

But, in truth, the circumstances surrounding his death remain a mystery.

It is likely that the Moroccan and Moorish interlopers were behind his murder. Samba's alliance with the French and the attempt – in the event, unsuccessful – to build a fort at Guiol may have been too much for the Moroccans and their Moorish allies. It is likely that they perceived these moves as an attempt by Samba to thwart the influence of the Ormans. Whatever the cause, it was not long after this episode, in 1741, that Samba was killed.

Samba was mourned throughout Bondu and far beyond, for he was a great man. I know that stories of his heroic exploits on his trusted mare, Oumoullatoma, and alongside his favourite griot, Sevi Malallaya, will be told and sung long into the future.

But I feel greatly privileged. To me he was a true and trusted friend with whom I had shared much of my life. It is my greatest regret that he would not be spared for us to stay together into our dotage.

By the end of the 1740s the Royal African Company's activities in Gambia were in a parlous state. A visitor to James Island, Captain Pye of *HMS Humber*, reported in 1749 that he found the fort in a most 'miserable condition'. He recorded that the people remaining on the island were in a 'melancholy situation for want of goods to carry on a trade for the support of their garrison, not having had any supplies for upwards of five years past and not being allowed to trade for themselves – the consequence of which was they were obliged to call in their outfactors on the continent, which were many, and, if properly supplied, one of the best branches of trade on the coast for wax, slaves, teeth and gold, but by being so long neglected the chief trade is gone down the River Senegal to the French factory'.

A merchant who visited the island the following year found the fort had been struck by 'so great a mortality' that numbers had been reduced to just 'five or eight' and a common soldier was now responsible for the security of the garrison. The flux and fever had decimated the island. So bad were the conditions that the captain of a visiting ship had ordered that no person should sleep ashore in the fort.

James Island was not alone in its suffering. The whole region suffered a series of droughts, resulting in poor harvests and famine. And recurring attacks by Moorish slave raiders just added to the general suffering and mortality.

I can only conclude that trading conditions, health risks aggravated by the climate and general unrest conspired against the fortunes of the Royal African Company throughout West Africa, because in that same year, 1750, the company's charter was withdrawn by an Act of Parliament. Within two years the company was closed in its entirety by another parliamentary act. It was the end of an era.

Looking back, I can only be thankful that the company – its leading officers and merchants – were there to make possible my redemption. Some may argue that I would not have been enslaved in the first place but for the activities of the company. But that would be wrong. There were many other entities both in Africa and from abroad willing to buy and trade slaves like myself. And I can never forget that by disobeying my father's instructions I was responsible for the capture of myself and Lamine Ndiaye. But having become a slave, I am sure I would never have been freed and returned home but for the Royal African Company.

I was so fortunate. From information I was able to glean in London and from conversations I have had with merchants in subsequent years, it appears the company was far from successful as a business entity. Even in 1730 – the year of my capture – the British government resorted to providing a subsidy of £10,000 to help the company continue its work.

Such subsidies of similar or much greater extent were provided annually until the end.

Coincidentally, at the same time the activities of the company were drawing to a close, the life of Mr Bluett, my very good friend and in so many ways the saviour of myself and Lamine Ndiaye, was also ending. Sadly, he died in Maryland in 1750.

As for myself, I progressed from middle age into the status of an ageing elder, respected for my wisdom, leadership and spiritual guidance. Above all else, I contented myself in my role as a priest and teacher, praising God daily that I had been spared to enjoy the company of my family and friends.

I often pondered on my extraordinary adventures and the challenges of my younger years, wondering whether they might become the stuff of legends, passed on by storytellers. I continued to take an interest in my community's farming activities, and I involved myself in trade from time to time. By this time, however, my sons had already established themselves as respected traders and I was quite happy to leave most of the negotiations to them.

Our trades were now with the newly formed Company of Merchants Trading to Africa, an enterprise established to succeed the Royal African Company, but with one major difference. This company was prohibited from trading in its own corporate capacity and obliged to trade with sundry African merchants. It was to our benefit that in the great seven years' war with France in the 1750s and early 1760s, the English took control of the French trading post at Fort St Joseph's. While I despise wars, this particular event brought me great satisfaction, partly because this was the wretched place where I was held captive and also because it was a closer trading post than those factories situated on the River Gambia.

From time to time, I was able to meet with travellers from

afar with whom I could share conversations in the English language. I was always happy to hear about the great men and women of England, and the developments taking place in that exciting city of London.

I have so much to be grateful for. That is why, over time and with the help of many literate friends, I set down this story. I also gave instructions to my sons and grandchildren that on my death they should ask a traveller to inform the Gentlemen's Society of Spalding of my passing and carry this text to London so that others might read the exploits of Ayuba Suleiman Diallo, an African slave who was freed to live a most extraordinary life.

But now, knowing that my days on Earth are coming to an inevitable end, it is time to reflect on how one stupid act, borne out of greed, disobedience and selfishness shaped my entire life. From the time of my capture by those Mandingo bandits to this very day, I have felt ashamed of the way I disobeyed my dear father and crossed that river to forbidden lands in search of greater trading gain.

It was punishment enough that I should be enslaved and made to suffer those early years of hardship. But my feelings of guilt and sadness were made so much worse by the knowledge that I had inflicted this unjustified punishment on my loyal friend Lamine Ndiaye. His hardship lasted much longer than mine. Throughout my life, even during those exciting times in England, I prayed for forgiveness. Unfortunately, I was never able to apologise to my father in person; I have lived with the scar of imagining how hurt he must have been, given my disobedience.

Throughout my time I have met with many great people, some of them standing at the highest level in their land, but no-one had been more influential than my dear father. For in his wisdom he taught me the way to live, through learning, hard work, respect for others and, most important of all, through adherence to Islam and its articles of faith. God has been with me throughout my life's journey – even when I made the wrong turn.

And there is no denying it was an extraordinary journey; one that took me from the simple, but still challenging, rural life in the Bondu region of West Africa to the most sophisticated houses and palaces in modern London and surrounds. The contrasts were bewildering and at times frightening. Those who lived and toiled in these two differing locations seemed to have been born in unrelated worlds in separate eras. And yet – when my English permitted – we conversed easily about our experiences, emotions and aspirations, demonstrating that essentially, we are all much the same in God's kingdom.

My eyes were opened – and, I confess, somewhat dazzled – by the trappings of modern living that I found in London: impressive houses with ingenious appliances and comfortable furnishings; horses with carriages to travel speedily in comfort from place to place; and clothing designed to appeal to the eye as well as provide warmth.

And yet with all the congestion, noise and foul smells that accompanied urban living I could not help but be homesick for the simpler – but equally rewarding – pleasures of life in Bondu. Here, at least, I could enjoy the sweet smells of the individual plants, feel the breeze on my face, and hear the sounds of the night. For all the excitement and flattery that I experienced in England, I realised that I felt more at ease, and at peace, facing natural dangers and challenges under the big skies and open spaces of West Africa.

That has been a paradox. Another has concerned my attitude to slavery. In this account of my life I have been honest with the feelings about my experiences. Indeed, as my language skills improved, I found that many of my friends and acquaintances in England were curious to hear how I, as one who once traded in slaves, felt about being enslaved myself. The simple answer was always 'I hated it!' Of course I did.

The cruelty meted out by uncouth traders and barbaric sailors was inhuman and unnecessary. The initial work that I was expected to carry out on the Maryland plantation was extremely arduous – a duty for which I was totally unsuited. When I was shown more respect and offered the task of looking after cattle, I performed well, given my experience as a pastoralist. And yet I was still determined to be freed, given my deep conviction that it was totally wrong and unjust for me to be enslaved.

I can still understand that slavery has a purpose – for providing the labour that would otherwise not be available. That is why I never turned my back on the practice. In my eyes, those who make themselves eligible for slavery are the captives in battle or those without learning and religion, who through their own inclination remain in the state and mentality of a savage.

As the years have passed, I admit that my mind has become increasingly troubled with doubt. As a young man, I accepted what I had been told was the natural order here in West Africa. In England I had come to appreciate that for some at least, the concept of slavery was at the least controversial.

Now I know I will not live to see the future. But perhaps one day there will be peace in this world, without the need for fighting, and everyone will have education and some fundamental belief to provide their own moral compass. Perhaps then the need for slavery will disappear and the process and consequences of the trade that I experienced, suffered and found personally to be so abhorrent, will no longer be required.

*The death, in 1773, of 'Job Jalla, Priest, at Bonda in Africa'
is recorded in an Appendix to the History of the Gentlemen's
Society at Spalding on page xxvi of the Bibliothetica
Topographica Britannica, published in 1791. Ayuba Suleiman
Diallo had lived to the age of seventy-two. The entry was
accompanied by a biographical note in which 'Job Ben Solomon
ben Abraham ben Abdulla' was described as a 'comely person,
near six feet high, pleasant but grave countenance, acute
natural parts, great personal courage and of so retentive a
memory that he could repeat the Koran by heart at 15, and
wrote it over three times in England by memory'.*[35]

In the Society's record of members Ayuba was recognised
as 'Job Jiallo or Dgiallo, High Priest of Bonda in Africa'. A
note in the publication *The Gentlemen's Society at Spalding:
Its Origin and Progress* by William Moore, the Society's
president in 1851, records, *'This person had been brought
over to England as a slave, but was redeemed from slavery by
subscription, and sent back loaded with presents. He translated
several Arabic manuscripts for Sir Hans Sloane, who got him
introduced at Court.'*

Notes

1   In Thomas Bluett's biography *Some Memoirs of the Life of Job*, Diallo's birthplace was called 'Boonda'. Francis Moore, in his Travels into the Inland Parts of Africa uses the spelling of 'Bundo'. Other published descriptions of the area have generally adopted Bondu, Bundu, Bondou or Boundou for the written version of what would have been a phonetic name. The Bondu spelling has been adopted in this book in the interest of consistency.

    The township where Diallo was born is unknown, although some sources have speculated it was a place called Bondu. Douglas Grant, in *The Fortunate Slave*, surmised from journeys undertaken by Ayuba in later life, that the birthplace might have been a township called Chambey in the neighbourhood of Youpé Amadi. Chambey was recorded in Thomas Hull's itinerary of his journey with Diallo to Bondu in 1735. As a result, I have chosen to use Chambey as the name Diallo used in this imagined autobiography. On the other hand, Professor Philip Curtin, author of *African Remembered*, argued the evidence created a presumption that Ayuba came from the present-day town of Marsa, about fifteen miles southeast of Bakel in the northeastern part of Bondu. His research found that the largest concentration in present-day Bondu of people bearing the name Diallo is in Marsa. The most prominent resident with this family name in more recent times was coincidentally Suleiman Diallo, who – like Ayuba's father – was the community's leader and Iman of the mosque in the 1850s. Curtin added, however, that people of Ayuba's social group – Muslim clerics with mercantile interests – were easily mobile and Ayuba may have lived in a number of different places. I tend to agree with Curtin.

2   While Ayuba may have avoided trading in slaves of his faith, it is an often-overlooked fact that Muslims accounted for a significant proportion of those forcibly shipped across the Atlantic. It is now believed that at the height of the slave trade in the eighteenth century, up to thirty per cent of the estimated seven million Africans enslaved in North America were Muslim. (See Thomas A. Tweed in *Islam in America: From African Slaves to Malcolm X*, National Humanities Centre; and Edward E. Curtis in *Muslims in America*, Oxford University Press, USA, 2009. Also Aisha Stacey in https://www.islamreligion.com/articles/10455/a-muslim-roots-of-american-slaves-part-1/.)

3   One such story – relevant to this history – is the legend of Samba Gueladio Diegui, a character introduced in the next chapter. There are many published versions of this legend available online and in published form; not surprisingly given that they all have their roots in Senegambia's oral tradition of story telling. A version of this legend, reproduced in full in pages 215-231, is based on the text contained in *African Tales*, compiled by Harold Scheub; University of Wisconsin Press, 2005. Another version is published in *Oral Epics from Africa*, edited by John William Johnson, Thomas A Hale and Stephen Belcher. Here, 'The Epic of Samba Gueladio Diegui' was narrated by Pahel Mamadou Baila. The English translation by Amadou Ly and Stephen Belcher comes from unpublished work by Amadou Ly.

4   The given names of Ayuba's wives are fictitious, to aid the familiarity of the first-person text. The author has not been able to trace any record of the wives' real names. However, the names of their children are known from published accounts.

5   In Thomas Bluett's *Some Memoirs of the Life of Job*, the Alpha was from Tombut, an alternative name for Timbuktu, some

600 miles from Diallo's home. Philip Curtin argued in *Africa Remembered* the description should be understood as 'an alpha from Bambuk'.

6   Thomas Bluett's *Some Memoirs of the Life of Job* states that the Alfa was from Tomga. In *Africa Remembered* Philip Curtin gives the location as 'Damga, the southeasternmost part of the Tukulor kingdom bordering on Bondu and Gadiaga'.

7   The Mandingo or Mandinka are an African ethnic group within the larger linguistic family of Mande-speaking people. Philip Curtin, in *Africa Remembered*, pointed out that Mandingo sometimes referred more narrowly to the Malinke, who lived on both banks of the lower Gambia.

8   There are various published versions of this interpreter's name. Thomas Bluett in *Some Memoirs of the Life of Job* styles him as Loumein Yoas. Douglas Grant in The Fortunate Slave preferred Loumein Yoai. In correspondence of the Royal African Company the name is given as Lahmin Jay. The spelling adopted in this book is taken from Philip Curtin's book *Africa Remembered* – Lamine Ndiaye. Curtin explains that Ndiaye is a Wolof name, but the Ndiaye family of Jollof origin had already established themselves as the dominant family of Bakel, about fifteen miles from Ayuba's home.

9   In 2011, the island was renamed Kunta Kinteh Island after a character in the novel *Roots: The Saga of an American Family* by American author Alex Haley. It was claimed that the character was based on an ancestor of Haley who was born in Gambia in 1750, enslaved and taken to America. Like Diallo, Kunta Kinteh was taken by slave ship to Annapolis, Maryland.

10 Thomas Bluett, in his *Some Memoirs of the Life of Job* names Ayuba's owner as 'Mr Tolsey in Kent Island'. The name is carried in many other works of reference that followed. The Christian name 'Alexander' was added in an account in the Spalding Gentlemen's Society *First Minute Book* (f.186). Research in the Maryland State Archives, including the specialist Study of the Legacy of Slavery in Maryland, throws no light on the existence of Mr Tolsey, although there is ample evidence in the archives that indicate Alexander Tolson is likely to have been Ayuba's owner. I have thus adopted this identity.

Mr Tolson was a plantation owner who was born in England in 1693. He died in Kent Island, Queen Anne's County in April 1741. Some records show the spelling of his name as Toulson. In his will Mr Tolson recognised six sons and two daughters: Andrew, Alexander, Joseph, Benjamin, John, James, Rachel and a married daughter, Susanna Stephens. Three hundred and fifty acres of land was bequeathed in equal proportions to Andrew, Alexander and Joseph. He left a negro woman to his wife, a negro girl called Phillis to his daughter Rachel, two negroes to James and two negroes to John. His son-in-law, John Stephens, was also bequeathed 'fifty pounds of tobacco'.

11   The location of the plantation is supposition, indicated by J.G. Strong's 1866 map of Queen Anne's County and Kent Island showing the location of properties owned by J.D. Tolson, J.C. Tolson and B.C. Tolson between the modern community of Stevensville and Chester River's Northeast Bay. Alexander Tolson's will indicates his land being adjacent to Philpotts Creek. The area next to 'a point called Philpotts' was bequeathed to his son Alexander with a note that he was at liberty to 'get timber' from the land. Kent Island is the largest island in the Chesapeake Bay, measuring twenty-one miles from north to south and seven miles wide. It was settled in 1631 and was the third English-speaking settlement in America, after Plymouth Rock and Jamestown.

12   This could be construed as the introduction of one of the first mosques in the US, according to Edward E. Curtis IV, Millennium Chair of Liberal Arts and Professor of Religious Studies at Indiana University-Purdue University Indianapolis and author of *Muslims in America: A Short History*. Responding to critics of a proposal to build a mosque close to Ground Zero in New York City, Professor Curtis wrote in the *Washington Post* on August 29, 2010, 'Mosques have been here since the colonial era. A mosque, or masjid, is literally any place where Muslims make salat, the prayer performed in the direction of Mecca; it needn't be a building. One of the first mosques in North American history was on Kent Island, Md. Between 1731 and 1733, African American Muslim slave and Islamic scholar Job Ben Solomon, a cattle driver, would regularly steal away to

the woods there for his prayers – in spite of a white boy who threw dirt on him as he made his prostrations.' However, it is inconceivable that salat was not performed in the New World long before this. Historian Sam Haselby recorded in the digital magazine *Aeon* in June 2019 that Muslims from West Africa were in the New World early in the sixteenth century. Christmas 1522 saw the New World's first slave rebellion when twenty sugar mill captives, mostly Wolofs from Diallo's Senegambian region, began slaughtering their Spanish slave masters.

13 This area, embracing the counties bordering the Delaware River and Delaware Bay, was administered by the government of New Castle, Kent and Sussex upon the Delaware at the time of Ayuba's incarceration in jail. The state did not use the single title of Delaware until 1776.

14 His name was unknown. The name Peter has been assigned to him for the sake of the narrative.

15 The description of the lodgings and host family are fictional, although it is quite possible that Diallo was housed in a merchant's home in Narrow Street. The Georgian houses, the inn (now called The Grapes and established in 1583) and St Anne's Church (consecrated in 1730) would all have been prominent in Limehouse at that time.

16 The only one of the three Korans penned by Ayuba Suleiman Diallo known to exist is in the El-Nimer collection, housed in Dar El-Nimer for Arts and Culture, in the heart of Beirut. The catalogue entry, written by Professor Alain George of the Khalili Research Centre for the Art and Material Culture of the Middle East, Oxford University, says the unique manuscript stands out as one of the oldest preserved African Korans. Prof. George points out that when composing sentences of his own, Ayuba used grammar that was not Arabic and feminine verbs were often used instead of the masculine form.

This is evident in the following translated passage from the opening text: 'In the Name of God, the Clement, the Merciful, say [the name of] God upon master Muhammad [shayyid muhammad], THE QUR'AN WHICH IS the Islamic law of Muhammad son of 'Abd Allah His name: she writes the Qur'an, God, Ayyub ibn Sulayman, Its name: the country of

Aqial Lindal [England London?]. country of the Christians [anshārā]. Book was completed on Thursday the sixteenth of the month of 'akith 1135, the end of Muhammad. Ayyub ibn Sulayman, country of Bundu. His name: his brother Hamad, Hamad [sic] ibn Sulayman Ahmad ibn Bubu. His name: the two women [?] Fulad [?] ibn Siddiq the mother of ibn Bubu Keita [?].' Prof. George states that the expression 'the end of Muhammad' probably means the 'the death of Muhammad', which would equate to around 1733 in the Gregorian era.

The Twelve Apostles are set down in Arabic and written in English pronunciation: *Bita* (Peter), *jims* (James), *jan* (John), *aduru* (Andrew), *filib* (Philip), *batalma mas* (Bartholomeus), *tamas* (Thomas), *jims* (James), *sadiyas* (Thaddeus), *sayman* (Simon), *judas* (Judas), *muthsayas* (Mattheus).

On the next page Ayuba wrote two verses of the Koran as an incipit or introduction to the manuscript: 'So woe to those who write the Book with their hands, then say, "This is from God", that they may sell it for a little price; so woe to them for what their hands have written, and woe to them for their earnings.' And: 'Who does great evil than he who forged against God a lie?' Prof. George makes the point that while the ills of forging scriptures are thus emphasised, the underlying intent remains unclear.

17 The white ensign was the second most senior ensign. Between 1620 and 1864 the Royal Navy was divided into three squadrons: Red, White and Blue. The Red Squadron, the most senior, patrolled the Caribbean and the North Atlantic. The White Squadron patrolled the coasts of Britain, France and the Mediterranean, and the Blue Squadron patrolled the South Atlantic.

18 Now known as the Chelsea Physic Garden.

19 Sir Hans Sloane's collection formed the basis of the British Museum, opened to the public in 1759. A large proportion of this collection then became the foundation of the Natural History Museum, opened in 1881.

20 Unfortunately, I have not been able to verify the location for this royal audience. While it is likely to have been in Kensington Palace, it is also possible that the nearby St James's Palace was

chosen as the venue. Kensington Palace was certainly the place where, in 1734, George II, Queen Caroline and their children granted an historic audience with a delegation of indigenous Americans from the Yamacraw nation, a Creek tribe of North American Indians whose lands were appropriated into the British colony of Georgia. The honour bestowed on Ayuba Suleiman Diallo was similar to that afforded the Yamacraw, born out of the royal family's interest in fostering conditions in which British imperial interests could thrive. Regrettably the audience with Ayuba was less well-publicised. The location, topic of conversation and the identity of all those present are not known. Hence, the details given in this account are largely my own, guided by various authorities, including Dr Joanna Marschner, Senior Curator, State Apartments, at Kensington Palace. Dr Marschner mentions that one of the later eighteenth-century accounts relates that perhaps Prince William might have been present during the audience. This may account for the Prince's interest in Ayuba, whom he later met. The Prince also donated to Ayuba's freedom fund.

21 It is doubtful if Ayuba was aware of the true scope of the Royal African Company's trading activities in West Africa, although in conversations he may have gleaned some information during his stay in African House. On October 31 the company held a General Court, the proceedings of which were later reported in the monthly *Political State of Great Britain*. The report stated that on profits made from trade in Africa, from October 6, 1729 to June 30, 1731, the gain from trade in the Gambia region amounted to £11,528. 2s. 9d. of which £3,458. 17s. 4d. was made from the trade of 1,077 'Negroes'. Ayuba and his friend Lamine Ndiaye would have accounted for two of this number. The report concludes, 'The Trade to Africa is allowed to be of as great Use and Importance as any Branch of Trade belonging to this Nation, and your Estate and Interest therein is of far greater Value than most People, and even than many of our own Body seem to imagine.' This again helps to explain why the company was keen to encourage Ayuba's assistance in this trade.

22 It is not recorded where Ayuba Suleiman Diallo dined with the

Duke of Montagu, but it is likely to have been in one of the Duke's fine homes he owned in London in the early eighteenth century. Records show that the Whitehall residence, a 'substantial house with outhouses and appurtenances', existed in April 1733. According to Crispin Powell, archivist of the Montagu archives and the Buccleuch Living Heritage Trust, the lease of the Bloomsbury mansion was held by Edward Montagu of Allerthorpe on February 4, 1731/2. This house would later be sold to become the first home of the British Museum. On this basis I have assumed the dinner was held at Montagu House, Whitehall, overlooking the River Thames.

23   £40,000 equates to more than £6 million in today's value, based on purchasing power. (Source: www.measuringworth.com.)

24   There is no evidence that Ayuba Suleiman Diallo did learn of these encounters, although it is possible. The information has been included in the interest of context.

25   While it is not known for certain that Ayuba Suleiman Diallo visited Ditton Park near Datchet, it seems likely. His biographer Thomas Bluett records that the Duke of Montagu 'was pleased to take Job often into the Country with him and shew him the Tools that are necessary for Tilling the Ground, both in Gardens and Fields, and made his Servants shew him how to use them'. The archives show that the Duke often entertained guests at Ditton Park. It is unlikely that the Duke took Ayuba to his other country residence, the grand Boughton House, much further away in Northamptonshire or to his comparatively modest Montagu House in less rural Blackheath. It was in Blackheath, that the former slave and writer Ignatius Sancho would serve the Montagu family as butler between 1749 and 1751. Sancho had previously worked for three maiden sisters in Greenwich.

26   The Koran manuscript presented to Joseph Smith first came to light in 2013 when it was featured by auctioneers Bonhams in a sale of Islamic and Indian Art. It was bought for the El-Nimer collection, now housed in the Dar El-Nimer for Arts and Culture, Beirut (see also note 16). According to Bonhams' lot description, the manuscript, comprising 223 leaves with twenty-one lines of script on each page, and bound in Moroccan leather, was previously held in private US collections.

Evidence that Joseph Smith was the original recipient is contained in one of three notes inserted at the beginning of the manuscript sometime in the eighteenth century, signed by 'Wm Smith'. It states: 'This Job when in London used to visit almost weekly at the House of Mr Joseph Smith my great-uncle, who then lived in Cannon Street in the City – anno 1733.' There is also a note in Latin with the signature 'Saml Chandler'. This note, that concludes with the Latin testimony translated as 'He [Job] was certainly a most pious and upright man, in step with the Christian faith' is verified by another note, signed by 'Wm Smith': 'This note is in the hand writing of Dr Samuel Chandler, a dissenting Minister of that time, whose character and writings are well-known.'

Professor Alain George of the Khalili Research Centre for the Art and Material Culture of the Middle East, Oxford University, who prepared the catalogue entry for the Dar El-Nimer collection, states: 'These pages show that, two generations after it was made, the manuscript had come into the possession of William Smith (1756–1835), an influential English Member of Parliament and Dissenter. William Smith is a common English name, but the identification is confirmed by an ex-libris on the inner cover that reads:

"Dr & Madam Bodichon 5, Blanford Square, N.W.

Barbara Leigh Smith Bodichon (1827–91), who married Dr Eugène Bodichon in 1857, was the granddaughter of William Smith, and a leading feminist and social activist of the Victoria era, and a painter. She used to winter in Algiers, and thus happened to have fostered connections of her own with the Arab world. Furthermore, William Smith's own father had been a wholesale grocer on Cannon Street, in London, which is associated here with 'Mr Joseph Smith my great-uncle'. Thus, it was William Smith who wrote two of the above notes; it is likely that he also added these three pages to the book, and had it set in its present gilt morocco binding, with gilt page-edges. Smith had probably come to know about Diallo not only through Bluett's book, but also through family memories. As Smith was a key figure in the Abolitionist movement, the present volume stands as a testimony to the role played by Diallo's story, after his death, in garnering support against slavery."

27   William Hoare (1707–1792) showed an aptitude for drawing at an early age and was sent to study under Giuseppe Grisoni in London. When Grisoni returned to his native Italy in 1728, Hoare went with him and moved to Rome, where he continued his studies under Francesco Imperiali. It is thought Hoare moved back to England in 1732/33. After pursuing his painting in London and Bath, he moved back to Italy for another spell before returning again to London in 1737/8. He later became one of the leading oil portraitists of his time. A foundation member of the Royal Academy, Hoare was commissioned to paint a number of the social leaders of the day, including Prime Ministers Robert Walpole and William Pitt, and composer George Frideric Handel. The Earl of Pembroke was among his powerful patrons. Today the portrait of Ayuba Suleiman Diallo is exhibited in the National Portrait Gallery, London, on long-term loan from the Qatar Museums Authority. Hoare's 'sensitive' portrait is described by the National Portrait Gallery as the earliest-known British oil portrait of a freed slave and the first portrait to honour an African subject as an individual and an equal.

28   While there has been speculation that the gown worn by Ayuba Suleiman Diallo in the portrait might have been the garment he wore for his audience at Court, I have been unable to find direct evidence for this.

29   In August 1750, in a retrospective note on archived correspondence, Maurice Johnson, as President of the Spalding Gentlemen's Society, recorded that Ayuba was an 'open, candid, humane & good man' who spoke English well enough to be understood and was skillful in writing Arabic quickly and readily. In addition, according to Maurice Johnson, Ayuba had knowledge of six dialects used in differing kingdoms of Africa.

30   Douglas Grant, in his book *The Fortunate Slave: An Illustration*

of African Slavery in the Early Eighteenth Century, spells the name of the emissary as Sir Randal Macdonald. The British Library, in its summary of Sir Hans Sloane's archives, documents him as 'Randal Macdonell, Captain of the Duc de Bourbon's Life Guards'. The archived document states in the original handwriting, 'Copy of a Letter from Sr Randal Macdonell to Sr Hans Sloane dated Chantilly May 25, 1734.' (British Museum Sloane MS 4053 f219.) It is accepted that around that time the name 'MacDonald' was spelt in several ways, including: MacDonald, McDonald, MacDonell, McDonnell.

31   Five hundred pounds equates to almost £80,000 in today's value, based on purchasing power. (Source: www.measuringworth. com.)

32   The intuition was fully justified, as demonstrated by a private letter, not shown to Ayuba that was sent in the packet of instructions. Dated July 4, 1734, the letter, from the company to Governor Richard Hill, reinforced the importance of the freed slave, Ayuba, pointing out that during his stay in England he had been recognised by the King and Queen and other prominent people. It was important that not only should every care be taken of his welfare but also his possessions should be protected from loss or embezzlement. The company was seeking to develop 'trade and Correspondence' between those parts of Africa and its highest factories. The letter stated, 'If the person you should send up river with him should be willing to accompany him into his own country, possibly he might by that means be able to do the Company good service by opening and settling a trade and correspondence between the natives of those parts and our highest factories.' The company's agents were requested to ensure that Ayuba himself should send a letter with the Dolphin on its return confirming 'that he had been well used by Capt. Freeman as well as while he stays with you'. The instructions indicated that while every effort was being taken to make a good impression on Ayuba, the company was not absolutely certain that he would in the end be willing to act as an agent for British trading interests.

33   It is likely that John Chandler was introduced to Ayuba by Sir Hans Sloane or one of his circle of acquaintances. A partner

in a firm of apothecaries, based at the corner of King Street in London's Cheapside, Chandler was drawn into the affairs of the Royal Society, like so many of those who Ayuba befriended. In 1729, Chandler published *A Discourse concerning the Smallpox*. He also presented several papers to the Society. Much later, in 1761, he published *A Treatise on the Disease Called Cold*. He was elected a fellow of the Royal Society in February 1735, being recommended as 'a gentleman well skilled in botany, anatomy and other parts of natural knowledge'. Another link with Sir Hans Sloane came through his interest in the Chelsea Physic Garden, where he served on the administration committee.

It is possible that Ayuba was welcomed into the wider Chandler family, for John Chandler was the younger brother of Samuel Chandler, the noted dissenting minister and theologian, who attested to Ayuba being a 'most pious and upright man, in step with the Christian faith' in a note that was found inserted in the Koran manuscript that Ayuba had presented to Joseph Smith (see note 26).

34   The Sisibe and Denianke dynasties held long-standing feuds over the kingdom of Bondu. Tribal wars were frequent, if often localised. Ayuba Suleiman Diallo's family were followers of the Denianke, which helps to explain that in his own memoir, written by Thomas Bluett, he made no mention of the Sisibe. The Sisibe dynasty can be traced back to Malik Si, a Fulani from a prominent religious family who was born in Futa Toro in the first half of the seventeenth century. He emigrated from Futa Toro to establish the ruling Sisibe dynasty. The Denianke dynasty is much older, established by Dengalla Koli in 1513, Originally the Denianke followed a traditional African religion which inceasingly brought them into conflict with the growing Muslim subjects of their realm. A summary of rulers in these two dynasties is shown in the table on pages 213-214. Much of the information is drawn from oral data and there remains much to be learned about chronologies, successions within the dynasties and the precise state of ruling authority within Bondu at any one time.

35   It is not known how the Gentlemen's Society of Spalding came to be informed of Ayuba Suleiman Diallo's death.

LOG OF A JOURNEY UNDERTAKEN BY THOMAS HULL
AND AYUBA SULEIMAN DIALLO

Stations	Miles	Bearings	Remarks
1. From Yamyamacunda to...			
2. Cowas	4	N.	a Small Town.
3. Mancadaway	10	E.	Formerly a large Town but was last year destroyed by Fire.
4. Suncobarr	12	N.E.	half-way is a remarkable Hill.
5. Concord	6	N.E.	The Capital Town in Wooley.
6. Cohunt or Count	8	N.E.	A Mahometan Town.
7. Sowro	7	N.	Formerly a large Town but lately destroy'd by yᵉ Warrs.
8. Colingding	5	N.N.E.	a Small Town but ruin'd by the Warrs.
9. Conophy	10	N.N.E.	a large & Strong Town.
10. Condery	8	N.E.	a small Town, 4 Miles East of this town lyes Cassang.
11. Cross'd yᵉ River Samy	10	N.N.E.	This River falls into yᵉ Gambia near Fendalecunda & is said to come out of yᵉ Senegal river.
12. Calore	6	N.E.	a Strong Town, the Master & Inhabitants are Slaves belonging to the King of Wooley.
13. Cambey	9	E.N.E.	a Strong Town & the last in the Kingdom of Wooley.
Carried Forward	95		

The log of the journey undertaken by Thomas Hull of the Royal African Company, along with Ayuba Suleiman Diallo, shown above and continued on the next page, is taken unedited from Hull's journal containing his 'Voyage to Bondou, 1735'. This journal was kindly made available by the archivist of the Montagu archives and the Buccleuch Living Trust at Boughton House, Northamptonshire.

Stations	Miles	Bearings	Remarks
Brought forward	95		
14. Cross'd Bajasa or Samy River again	7	E.	
15.	3	E.	
16.	10	E.by S.	
17.	6	E.S.	A large Wilderness
18	14	E.S.E.	which we were four
19. a River	4	E.	days & 3 Nights going
20.	4	N.E.	thro'.
21. Scitadella, a large Pond or Spring of good Water & never dry	3	N.E.	
22. River Galore	7	E.	
23. Goodery	7	E.by N.	A Town in a province so call'd belonging to Bundo, its Lat. is 14.33, about one Mile before we came to this Town we cross'd the River Neery or Yarico, which falls into the Gambia at Tinda.
24. Wild	5	E.	a small Town.
25. Bullabuck	15	N.E.	a small Town.
26. Chambey	5	E.	Job's houses or Hutts are in this Town, its Latit. is 14.44. North & from whence I could plainly hear ye Guns at ye French Fort at Gallam.
From Chambey to...			
Phenah	8	S.	A large Town where lives Eleman Maccah King of Bundo.

Conjure	6	E.N.E.	a Town almost close to Fallam River which parts Bundo from the Kingdoms of Gallam & Bombou; Its Inhabitants are Merchants chiefly & is situate not far from the opposite side of the River where the Sanon Colez, or as the French call it, Riviere D'or falls into it, & on which the Gold Mines border; which Mines supplies the Gold Trade to ye French on the Senegall, which is a very considerable one & to all parts Inland and to the River Gambia; The Inhabitants of Goodery, Bundo, Futa & Boumbou & most of the other Inland Countrys are Mahometans.

Ayuba Suleiman Diallo: Timeline

◇◇◇

Born: Bondu, Senegambia 1701
Married first wife: 1716
Married second wife: 1729
Captured and traded as slave: Feb 1730
Shipped as a slave to Maryland: 1730
Escaped from owner, recaptured and jailed: June 1731
Freed from jail and bonded to Captain Henry Hunt: 1732
Shipped to England: March 1733
Lodged in Limehouse, London: May 1733
Met with leading members of British Society: 1733
Portrait painted by William Hoare of Bath: 1733
Met with Envoys of the Bey of Tunis: Dec 1733
Audience with King George II and Queen Caroline: Early 1734
Proposed as a member of Spalding Gentlemen's Society: May 1734
Elected as a member of Spalding Gentlemen's Society: June 1734
Sailed from England to return to Africa: July 1734
Arrived at Fort James, Gambia: Aug 1734
Told about the death of his father: Feb 1735
Returned to his home town : July 1735
Captured by the French; imprisoned in St Joseph's Fort: June 1736
Part of gifts from England lost in shipwreck: 1736
Remainder of gifts lost in Yamyamacunda fire: Aug 1736
Released from St Joseph's Fort: Early 1737
Made unsuccessful plea to return to England: 1740
Royal African Company's charter withdrawn: 1750
Died, aged seventy-two: 1773

Early rulers of competing Futa Toro and Bondu dynasties

◇◇◇

Sisibe Dynasty
(descendants of Malik Si… up to the end of Ayuba Suleiman Diallo's lifetime)

Malik Si	c1693–1699
Bubu Malik Si	c1699–1715
Interregnum – Sisibe were without power	1716–1720s/30s
Maka Bubu Malik Si	1730s
Maka Jiba	c 1730s–c1760s
Samba Tulane (reigned for brief period only)	c1764
Amadi Gai	1764–1786

Denianke Dynasty
(descendents of Dengella Koli I in the sixteenth century… up to the end of Ayuba Suleiman Diallo's lifetime)

Bubakar Sawa Lamu (Bubakar Tabakali)	1640–1669
Sire Tabakali	1669–1702
Samba Bohi	1702–1707
Samba Dundu	1707–1709
Bubakar Sire Samba Lamu	1709–1710
Gueladio Jegi	1710–1718
Bubakar Sire Samba Lamu (second reign)	1718–1721
Bubu Musa	1721–1722
Bubakar Sire Samba Lamu (third reign)	1722–1723

Bubu Musa (second reign)	1723–1724
Samba Sire Samba Lamu	1724
Bubu Musa (third reign)	1724–1725
Samba Gueladio Diegui	1725–1726
Konko Bubu Musa	1726–1738/40
Samba Gueladio Diegui (second reign)	1738/40–1741
Konko Bubu Musa (second reign)	1741–1743
Sule Bubu Musa (Sule Ndiaye I)	1743–1747
Bubu Gaisiri	1747–1749
Sule Bubu Musa (Sule Ndiaye I) (second reign)	1749–1750/51
Jaje Ule	1750/51–1752
Sule Bubu Musa (Sule Ndiaye I) (third reign)	1752–1765
Samba Bohi Konko	1765–1772
Bokar Sule	1772
Makhan Uru	1772
Sule Bubu Musa (Sule Ndiaye I or possibly Sule Ndiaye II)	1772–1776

Note: information collected from various sources, but most notably from *A Tentative Chronology of the Futa Toro from the Sixteen through the Nineteen Centuries*. Robinson, Curtin and Johnson (see bibliography).

Legend of Samba Gueladio Diegui

◇◇◇

This is the story of Samba Gueladio Diegui, a renowned warlord, ruler of Futa Toro and Bondu, and a close friend of Ayuba Suleiman Diallo. It is a popular African tale that is told, or rather performed, by griots and other storytellers even today, both as entertainment and as a reminder of history and tradition. Inevitably there are many versions of this legend (certainly more than a dozen), given that the original content was always committed to memory and acted out with appropriate gestures and emphasis. Thus, transcribing these tales from the oral form to the written word and then from an African language into English was always a painstaking task. This version of the Samba Gueladio Diegui legend is based largely on the text published in Harold Scheub's book, African Tales, although adjustments have been made to conform with spellings and style adopted in the rest of this book. Other notable translations include those by Amadou Ly and Amadou Abel Sy.

Samba was the only son of Gueladio, King of the Futa region, who suffered the blow of his father's death when he was still a teenager. It was Gueladio's brother Konko Bubu Musa who took control of the country. Konko Bubu had eight sons, and when they grew to manhood, he announced he would share Futa among them.

On hearing this news from Sevi Malallaya, his griot, Samba immediately went to his uncle and asked, 'Where is my share?'

'I am going to give you something, too,' responded Konko Bubu. 'The first horse you see in the Futa – take it. It is yours.'

On advice from Sevi, Samba declined the offer, saying, 'I don't want your present. It is not what I need. Give me what is due to me. I do not ask for anything else.'

Konko Bubu then said he had seen a fine bull and a beautiful woman in the Futa. 'Take them both. I make you a present of them.'

'It is worthless,' advised the griot. 'It is like what he gave you before. If you find a beautiful woman who is married, and you take her, her husband will kill you. You are a child and you do not understand.'

Samba again declined the offer. 'What I want is my share of Futa.'

'If you really want it,' retorted Konko Bubu, 'you had better set about taking it. If not, so much the worse for you.'

Samba went away and saddled up his mare Oumoullatoma. He then set off with his mother, his griot and his griot's mother, his slave Doungourou, and the slaves destined to be his wives, for at that time he was not married. 'I am going to leave Futa,' he said.

His first stop was in a village called Tiabo, close to Bakel. There he called on the local ruler, Tounka, to whom he entrusted his mother and the mother of his griot. 'Give them food and clothes, and lodge them well in good houses,' said

Samba. 'Otherwise, when I return and find they have lacked clothing and food, I will cut off your head.'

Without further delay, Samba and his remaining party continued their journey for the lands administered by a king called Ellel Bildikri. Samba was intending to ask the king to send warriors to attack Konko Bubu Musa.

After walking through forests for forty-five days, they reached the land of the Fulani. Here, after being welcomed in a royal manner, the local king invited Samba to relax in the company of his daughters. After feasting, the girls went off to bathe while Samba laid down on his bed to rest. One of the young girls had taken off her gold necklace and left it in the house, but while Samba was sleeping it was swallowed by an ostrich. When the girls returned, they woke Samba and asked about the missing necklace, inferring he may have taken it. Samba then spotted the tracks of the ostrich's feet.

'I will give you a calabash of gold if you sell me your ostrich,' Samba told the king.

The king agreed, and Samba ordered men to kill the ostrich. 'When you have killed it, open its body and bring us whatever you find inside.' The men did as he wished and found the necklace in the bird's stomach.

Samba turned to the girl who owned the necklace and said, 'You accused me of stealing the necklace. I shall have you put in chains.' The king left him to do as he pleased.

But Sevi, the griot, intervened. 'You are wrong to act like this, Samba. We have left our country to come here and there are only five of us. Leave the king's daughter alone and don't seek to make her captive.'

Samba heeded Sevi's advice and the next day they continued their journey to the kingdom of Ellel Bildikry. They continued walking through bush and forest, and after fifteen days they ran short of water supplies.

'I cannot move forward. I will die,' said Sevi, the griot. Samba led Sevi and his slave Doungourou to the shade of a tree and told them to wait for him. Samba then mounted his mare and rode for two hours before finally arriving at a pool. There he encountered a very tall bogy – an evil spirit – taking a bath.

Turning to Samba, the bogy burst into fire. But Samba was not afraid. He looked the spirit straight into his face. The bogy then made himself so tall he seemed to touch the sky with his head.

'What are you doing now?' Samba asked quietly. 'Do you want to see if I am afraid of you?'

The bogy became smaller and said, 'Never have I seen a man as brave as you. I am going to give you a present.' And he handed Samba a gun, naming it Boussalarbi. 'You only need to take it out of its holster and your enemy will fall dead.'

Samba then took his goatskin and entered the pool to collect water. Just as he was about to leave, he thought he would test if the bogy was telling the truth about the gun. On taking the gun out of its holster the bogy fell dead.

When he returned to his colleagues, Samba related the story of what had happened at the pond. 'That was wrong,' said the griot. 'It was very wrong what you did there! You killed someone who made you a present like that. You acted very unjustly.'

'I did well,' replied Samba. 'If I happened to pass that way, others might pass as well. I am not the only king's son. Futa has many kings and many brave ones among them. Today the bogy gave this gun to me, and tomorrow he would have done the same to any other. He has finished making gifts now. Nobody will have a gun like mine. I am the only one to have such a wonderful weapon.'

After this they decided to travel on, arriving after several days at Ellel Bildikri's capital. They soon learnt that for nearly a year the village had been without fresh drinking water. They were told a large crocodile in the river prevented the people from drawing water. Each year a well-dressed young girl adorned with golden jewellery was presented to the river, but this crocodile was very demanding, refusing their offering and forbidding them to renew their annual water supply.

It so happens that it was the last day of the year when Samba and his colleagues arrived in the village and the local inhabitants were preparing to make such an offering to the crocodile called Niabardi Dallo.

Around midnight, a little way from the village, Samba asked a local slave for a drink of water to quench his thirst. On receiving a cup of water, and finding it foul-smelling, Samba struck the slave who fell to the ground.

'I ask you for water and you bring me filth like this,' cried Samba.

'My friend,' answered the woman. 'There is no more water in the country. Before we can have any more, we must sacrifice the king's daughter.'

Samba then asked to be directed to the river. 'I want my mare to drink,' he said.

The slave was frightened and refused to lead them to the river. But Samba insisted, 'If you refuse to take me, you will die at my hand.' Doungourou was told to take the mare's halter and the slave was made to walk in front.

When they arrived near the river, Samba took pity on the slave because of her fear. Thanking her, he allowed her to return home. Samba then ordered Doungourou to strip and enter the water with the horse. Immediately Niabardi Dallo, the crocodile, called out.

'Who's there?' he cried.

'This is a new arrival,' replied Samba.

'Well, newcomer. What are you doing here?'

'We come to drink!' said Samba.

'If you have come to drink, you must drink alone and don't let your horse drink,' said the crocodile.

Samba stood his ground. 'The newcomer is going to give the mare a drink,' he said.

Samba and his slave drank and then Doungourou was instructed to enter the river with the mare. The horse paddled the water with her hoof.

'You annoy me,' said the crocodile. Niabardi rose in the river, opening his jaws widely, and all the water around him shone like fire.

Samba shouted to his slave, 'If you're afraid of what you see and you let go of my mare, I'll kill you along with the crocodile.' The slave held on tightly.

The crocodile came towards them, his jaws wide open with fire spouting from his throat. When he was quite near Samba shot him. The crocodile was killed, and the whole river turned the colour of blood.

Now that Niabardi Dallo was dead, Samba filled his goatskin bag with water and they returned to the house to take some rest. They gave some of their water to the slave of the house they were sharing.

'Where have you managed to get so much water?' she asked.

'Your tongue is too long,' Samba replied. 'You have the water. All you have to do is drink it without worrying where it comes from.'

After killing the crocodile, Samba cut off a piece to take with him. He also left behind bracelets and a sandal, because he knew very well that no-one else would be able to wear them. Samba's feet were very small.

The next day Ellel Bildrikry summoned all the griots to take a sacrificial girl to the crocodile so that residents would be permitted to collect fresh water. They set the young virgin on a horse and the griots followed her, singing, 'Oh young girl, how brave you are. The crocodile ate your sister. He ate your other sister too. And yet you're not afraid of him. We will now have water!'

The griots sang aloud. They sang of the hundred victims that the beast had eaten.

When they reached the river, they led the young girl down to the water. Formerly, the other young girls had waded a little way into the water and the crocodile had come and snapped them up. On this day, the girl waded out until the water reached her chest. She climbed onto the head of the crocodile and cried out, 'The crocodile is here and I am standing on his head.'

And the people said, 'The crocodile is angry. You must have had relations with a man! You are no longer a virgin! Oh, what a misfortune! It is an evil day for us. You are a shameless girl!'

They immediately went and fetched another girl but the girl in the river defended herself indignantly. 'You are lying,' she said. 'No man has touched me since the day I was born. I have never shared a man's bed!'

The other young girl consented to be sacrificed and climbed up on to the crocodile. Now both were standing on the beast's head. And her father declared, 'The crocodile is dead!'

'Let everyone go into the river,' the king ordered. 'We shall see if it is true or not.'

Everyone went in and found it really was true.

'Well,' said the king, 'the first person who says he killed the crocodile and can prove it shall have whatever he asks of me.'

Immediately there were those who made such false claims, such as 'It is I who killed him', 'It was me who came here last night', and 'The crocodile wanted to eat me, so I killed him'. Each told his story to persuade the king he was the one who had slain the beast and should be entitled to the reward.

Then a slave who was there picked up the bracelets and the sandal and said, 'Here are the victor's bracelets and here is his sandal. It is the man to whom these belong who killed the crocodile. It is he who should receive the reward!'

'That's good,' said the king. 'The one who can put on these bracelets and sandal, with them fitting, is the one who killed the crocodile. He shall receive a reward!'

Many tried the test, but no-one succeeded. Then the slave girl stepped forward.

'There is a newcomer here,' she said. 'He came to my house and asked for water. I gave him some, but it was putrid and he struck me. He then went outside and was away for three hours, and when he returned, he gave me some fresh water. You need only to call him to find out what happened. As for me, I'm sure it was he who killed the crocodile.'

The king then sent men to fetch the stranger. They found Samba asleep in his bed and gave him a slap to wake him. Furious at being disturbed, Samba kicked the messengers and they left. Then the king sent another man to try and wake him.

'Let me sleep,' shouted Samba. 'If anyone else is sent to me, I will kill him!'

The envoy returned and told the king what had happened.

'Very well,' said the king. 'I will wait until he has had his sleep.'

They waited two hours. At last Samba woke and went to the river.

Samba greeted the king, who responded in similar fashion. The king offered Samba a seat beside him, inviting him to take his ease. Then, taking the bracelets and the sandal, the king asked, 'Do these belong to you?'

Samba took the other sandal from his pocket and put them both on his feet.

'Well,' said the king, 'you must come and stay with me.'

And Samba was provided with a very large house – more a palace.

The king sent men to fetch Samba's belongings and together with his companions and mare, all were installed in the king's enclosure. Many sheep were killed for feasting.

Samba stayed two months with the king, accompanied by young girls all the time. At the end of this time, the king called his guest and asked him about the purpose of his visit. 'What is it you want?' he asked.

'I need only fighting men,' replied Samba.

Ellel Bildikry summoned all his chiefs and told them, 'The slayer of the crocodile asks us to give him warriors.'

'Go all the way into the Futa?' protested the nobles. 'How can we do that?'

'This man has come all the way from the Futa,' the king replied. 'He has reached us here. For a year we were unable to fetch fresh water and this man killed the monster that prevented us from drinking. All he asks in return are fighting men. We cannot possibly refuse him.'

'Well,' replied the chiefs, 'this is what we will do. There is a king called Birama N'Gourori. Let us send Samba Gueladio Diegui to take his herd of cattle and make us a present of them. Then we will let him have his warriors and we will go with him into his country to make war.'

Now the only objective of this strategy was to rid themselves of Samba through false promises. They reckoned that he would lose his life in the attack on Birama N'Gourori because this king was very powerful.

To reach Birama N'Gourori's country Samba had to walk for more than eight days and cross at least eighteen streams and backwaters. Birama's herds were guarded by 300 herdsmen, each dressed in red trousers and jackets, red caps and red boots. They were all mounted on fine white horses.

After crossing the final marshes Samba approached the men. 'I am going to take your cattle,' he said.

'You are crazy,' they answered. 'Before you take the cattle, you will have to kill us all.'

'Come on,' Samba ordered. 'Walk before me and drive the cattle where I tell you.'

The herdsmen refused to obey him. They fell on Samba with spears in hand. Time and again they struck him, but the spears were just glanced aside without penetrating him, so powerful was his juju spirit.

Samba killed all the herdsmen with the exception of just one.

Samba took the captive he had spared, cut off his ears and then told him, 'Find Birama N'Gourori and tell him I have taken his cattle.'

The herdsman went to the large house of Birama. He asked the first person he encountered to tell the king about the killing of the herdsmen and the capture of his cattle. 'No, I don't want to!' was the reply.

At the time, the king was sleeping. One of his wives, who was dressing her hair in the Fulani fashion, asked, 'How can you give such news to Birama?' Others suggested that griots should be assembled.

Then they gathered hamond from the bushes. Hamond is a perfumed gum that the Wolof people call houmounguene or thiouraye. The fumes were wafted over Birama and he woke up.

The king saw the griots all making music on their stringed instruments and asked, 'What is it? What is all this about?

A man advanced, trembling. 'A Fulani came to your herdsmen. He wanted to take your cattle…'

He had no time to complete the sentence before he was killed by Birama.

'Allah himself cannot steal my cattle!' the king shouted angrily.

Another man approached and told the king what had happened. The king killed him too. He killed three like this and the others ran away.

Then Birama's sister entered, bringing with her some curdled milk. She set the drink before him saying, 'This is all you have left to eat now because the Fulani has taken your cattle. There is nothing left to give you.'

The king mounted his horse Golo, a chestnut, and rode off in fury. Behind the village he encountered Samba.

Samba stopped the cattle and waited for him quietly.

'Is it you who stole my cattle?' asked the king.

'Yes, it was me. But I will leave you a few if it makes you happy. I will keep the rest for myself.'

'You might do so,' said Birama, 'but you will have to kill me first.'

Samba then took out his pipe. He struck his flint, lit the pipe and took several puffs.

'Well, take your time. Decide as you please.' This was the way he spoke to the king.

Birama thrust his spear firmly against Samba, but it snapped in two. He snatched up another spear and struck again. The king thrust all his spears until he had only one left unbroken.

Then Samba struck in turn. And his spear broke as well.

Samba jumped on his mare and they both fought on horseback, with each of their horses also biting and fighting furiously.

Finally, Samba won and Birama quickly rode away.

They both raced to Birama's place, which comprised at least eight enclosures, each with its gate. As Birama arrived first his men let him enter and then they fired on Samba. Until the smoke from the gunfire had cleared the men could only surmise that Samba had fallen. But it was not so. When the smoke cleared, they saw him still chasing the king.

At each gate the same thing happened until Samba and Birama reached the middle of the houses.

'If it were not for your sister's protection, I would kill you,' said Samba. 'But I am of her Fulani blood and I cannot refuse her request when she has done me no wrong.'

Samba returned to the herd, counted out three hundred cattle, and sent them back to the king, saying, 'This is a gift that I make to Birama and his sister.'

'You are a Fulani like me,' Samba told the king. 'I do not want you to be reduced to feeding on curdled milk.'

Samba then departed, taking with him what he had kept of the king's herd.

When he reached Ellel Bildikri's village, he said, 'Here are Birama N'Gourori's cattle.'

'That's good,' said the king.

Samba told the king that he had been challenged to kill the crocodile Niabardi Dallo. This he had done. He had been told to seize the herds of Birama. 'We were warned that no-one would be able to take them and if we went to war we would perish. But again, I have succeeded. Now it is your turn to provide me with fighting men.'

The local women cried out, 'Because our husbands are afraid to go with you, it is we who will go with you; we women.'

But Ellel Bildikry summoned Samba and promised he would have men in a few days. The king then ordered the cutting of large tree trunks to make platforms. Samba saw that on each platform riders and horses were being assembled. The king explained that when the wood was worn by the horse's feet, it should be taken as a sign that sufficient horsemen had passed.

After a few days Samba said, 'That is enough. 'We must go now.'

Samba then set off for the Futa. As he approached, he ordered his columns of warriors to continue their march and head for N'Guiguilone, following the bank of the river.

Then Samba went to see his mother who had been entrusted to Tounka. Little did he know that the day he had left his mother to go to Tiyabo in the Futa, Tounka had said, 'Samba will surely be lost in the bush,' and he had expelled Samba's mother and companions from the village.

Samba's slaves had taken loincloths to make a tent to protect his mother from the sun and then they went into the bush to look for wheat. Whenever they saw a man collecting his harvest, they waited to pick up the little grain he left behind. Thus, Samba's mother was fed on a poor type of couscous and boiled leaves from trees.

Suddenly some of the slaves who had stayed with the mother heard the screams of Sevi, the griot. 'I am afraid for Samba. I respect him as my master. But his voice is loud and clear.' Then they heard singing.

The slaves cried, 'It is a herald we hear! Undoubtedly Samba is arriving!'

'Yes, it seems that my son is singing,' said the mother, adding sadly, 'it is the griot who sings well, because my son is lost. I will never again see my boy again.'

But at that moment Samba came into sight, mounted on his mare Oumoullatoma.

On seeing the plight of his mother and companions, Samba said, 'What does this mean?'

'You see, my son, how Tounka has treated us since you went away.'

Samba then went in search of Tounka. 'Where is Tounka?' he asked his people.

'Tounka is long dead,' came the reply, for the king had instructed his people to give such an answer if Samba ever came back.

'Then take me to his grave,' said Samba. 'If he is dead, I am going to light a fire and burn him.'

He was taken to a nearby place and told, 'Here is where the Tounka is buried.'

Samba called his men and ordered them to dig. But nothing was found.

'Now, bring him from of his house. I want him,' Samba commanded.

Tounka was then dragged from the centre of the village.

Samba, who was still mounted on his mare, took the branch of a tree and, stretching out his arm, said, 'Make a pile of jewellery, gold and fabrics until the heap is as high as my hand.'

When the pile was the height of one yard, the griot Sevi shouted, 'It is not high enough. Bring some more.' Sevi then began to flatten the mound until Samba said, 'That is enough!'

Samba then addressed Tounka. 'Another time, if I leave my mother in your care remember what I have just done. Or wait until I catch you again.' He took the cloths, fabrics and gold and gave them to his mother and his people. And then he set off again.

Passing through Quahoulde in Futa, he rejoined his warriors by the N'Guiguilone. From there he sent a message to his uncle, Konko Bubu, telling him to be ready to fight him at Bilbaci.

At that moment Konko Bubu was at Sadel, near Kayaedi. Samba went to him and found his uncle waiting with his army.

In those days before a battle, the combatants held a great war dance. The big war drum used by the griots was called Alamari. Only brave men who had no fear were permitted to take part in the dance they danced. The dance was also called Alamari and the men danced with spear in hand.

The war drum was covered with the skin of a young girl. Samba, hearing the beat of the drum, said, 'I want to go there too, I want to dance Alamari!'

His griot, Sevi Malallaya, said, 'Are you crazy? You must stay here until tomorrow.'

Samba replied, 'Say what you like. I don't care. I am going!'

Samba crossed the river. He went as far as the war dance and joined the circle of onlookers. He covered his head with his waist cloth to hide his face and went and danced with spear in hand.

Each said to himself, 'But that is Samba Gueladio Diegui!'

Samba never breathed a word. He was in the war dance.

He called his cousins, the sons of Konko Bubu Musa, and said, 'Come! Let us go to your father's house. We will talk there together.'

There was a slave named Mahounde Gali who had a bad eye. His son asked him, 'Father, how can you go and fight tomorrow in that state?'

'Bring me a kilo of capsicum,' his father replied. He spread the capsicum on his bad eye and kept it there with a bandage. Then he lay down to rest. When he took off the bandage, his eye was as red as fire. 'When Samba's army sees a man with an eye all fiery red, they will flee in terror,' he said.

At six o'clock in the morning, Samba's warriors and those of Konko Bubu began to fight. Samba was still lying down in Konko Bubu Musa's house. He had spent the night laughing and joking with his cousins. At sunrise he said, 'Bring me water to wash myself.' He said this in front of everyone.

Then he took his spear and went out from the village. He crossed the columns of Konko Bubu Musa and went towards his own fighters. He found his mare tethered to a post and ordered a slave to saddle her. He mounted and set off at a gallop.

Samba entered Konko Bubu's ranks and drew his Boussalarbi gun from its holster. Each time he shot, he killed at least fifty warriors.

'What?!' cried Konko Bubu's fighters. 'In the beginning of the battle we thought that Samba's men would flee. But not at all! They are still holding their ground!'

So discouraged were Konko Bubu's men that they deserted their leader. You should have seen how they ran!

But Konko Bubu was not one to run away. When his horse fell dead, he collected earth and then filled his trousers. If he had wanted to run away and save himself, he couldn't, because the earth was too heavy.

Samba killed all before him.

And now he came face to face with Konko Bubu, standing near his dead horse.

'Well, Uncle, what has happened?'

'You can see,' said Konko Bubu. 'They have killed my horse.'

Samba ran after one of Konko Bubu's horsemen and killed him. He then returned with the horse and said, 'Uncle – get on this horse and keep on fighting.'

Konko Bubu mounted the horse and rushed towards Samba's columns. And his second horse was struck and fell dead.

Samba went to him again and said, 'Well, Uncle, have they killed another horse for you?' And he went to kill another of Konko Bubu's horsemen.

'Here, Uncle. Here is a new mount for you.'

Samba went on to replace at least eight horses that were killed under his uncle. He killed Konko Bubu's boys and slaughtered everyone. Now he was the ruler of Futa.

He led his uncle away from the village and said, 'Stay here. From now on you will beg charity from me.'

◇◇◇

When Samba himself finally died, they buried him in the ground. A Fulani passed near his grave and saw the ancient king's head sticking out from the earth.

'Ah,' he said. 'There is the head of a pig that thinks he isn't dead.'

He then took a stick and struck the skull with it.

The stick broke, and a flash of lightning pierced the Fula's eye and killed him.

It was said in the Futa that, 'Samba cannot die. It is he who killed the Fula.'

Selected bibliography

Al-Ahari, Muhammed A. *Job Ben Solomon's Handwritten Qur'ān* Found. Magribine Press, Chicago. 2013.

Al-Badaai, Muna Sulaiman. Positioning the Testimony of Job Ben Solomon, An Enslaved African American Muslim. *International Journal of Applied Linguistics and English Literature.* Vol. 4 No. 6. November 2015.

Alryyes, Ala (translator and editor). *The Life of Omar Ibn Said.* University of Wisconsin Press. 2011.

Austin, Allan D. *African Muslims in Antebellum America – Transatlantic Stories and Spiritual Struggles.* Routledge, New York and London. 1997.

Barry, Boubacar. *Senegambia and the Atlantic Slave Trade.* Cambridge University Press. 1998.

Belcher, Stephen. Constructing a Hero: Samba Gueladio Djegui. *Research in African Literatures.* Vol. 25. No. 1. Spring 1994 pp 75–92. Indiana University Press. 1994.

Bertrand, Alicia Marie. *The Downfall of the Royal African Company on the Atlantic African Coast in the 1720s.* History Master of Arts graduate thesis. Trent University, Peterborough, Ontario. October 2011.

Bluett, Thomas. *Some Memories of the Life of Job, the Son of the Solomon, the High Priest of Boonda in Africa; Who was a Slave about two Years in Maryland; and afterwards being brought to England, was set free, and sent to his native Land in the Year 1734.* Richard Ford, London. 1734.

Brooks, E. St John. *Sir Hans Sloane – The Great Collector and his Circle.* The Batchworth Press, London. 1953.

Bruce, Henry. *Life of General Oglethorpe.* Dodd, Mead, and Company, New York. 1890.

Bulliet, Richard W; Crossley, Pamela Kyle; Headrick, Daniel R; Hirsch, Steven W; Johnson, Lyman L; Northrup, David. *The Earth and Its Peoples; A Global History. Vol II: Since 1500.* Wadsworth Cengage Learning. Boston, Mass. 2011.

Campbell, James T. *Middle Passages – African American Journeys to Africa 1787–2005;* Penguin Books. 2007.

Cannadine, Sir David (editor). *Oxford Dictionary of National Biography.* Oxford University Press. 2019.

Clark, Andrew F. The Fulbe of Bundu (Senegambia): From Theocracy to Secularization. *The International Journal of African Historical Studies,* Vol. 29, No. 1. 1996.

Christie's. *Lot description (Lot 20/Sale 7782) for the sale of Portrait of Ayuba Suleiman Diallo, painted by William Hoare of Bath,* R. A. London. December 2009.

Collier, Sir G. R. and MacCarthy, Sir Charles (compiled from their reports and other sources). *West African Sketches.* L. B. Seeley and Son, London. 1824.

Conder, Josiah. *A Dictionary of Geography, Ancient and Modern of All the Countries of the Globe.* Thomas Tegg and Son, London. 1834.

Curtin, Philip D (editor). *Africa Remembered; Narratives by West Africans from the Era of the Slave Trade.* The University of Wisconsin Press, Madison, Milwaukee, and London. 1967.

Davies, K. G. *The Royal African Company.* Longmans, Green and Co. Ltd., London. 1957.

De Beer, Sir Gavin. *Sir Hans Sloane and the British Museum.* Oxford University Press, London. 1953.

Diène, Doudou (editor). *From Chains to Bonds – The Slave Trade Revisited.* Berghahn Books and UNESCO Publishing. 2001.

Diouf, Sylviane A. *The Servants of Allah. African Muslims Enslaved in the Americas.* 15th Anniversary Edition. New York University Press, New York and London. 2013.

Edwards, Jack. *Cheshunt in Hertfordshire.* Cheshunt Urban District Council. 1974.

Gibbs, F. W. Cromwell Mortimer, F.R.S.: Secretary, Royal Society, 1730–1752. *Notes and Records of the Royal Society of London*. Vol. 7, No. 2 pp 259–263. April 1950.

Gomez, Michael A. *Pragmatism in the age of Jihad – The precolonial State of Bundu*. Cambridge University Press, African Studies Series. 1992.

Grant, Douglas. *The Fortunate Slave: An Illustration of African Slavery in the Early Eighteenth Century*. Oxford University Press, London. 1968.

Gray, J. M. *A History of the Gambia*. Cambridge University Press. 1940.

Gray, Richard (editor). *The Cambridge History of Africa*, Vol. 4, c1600–1790. Cambridge University Press. 1975.

Green, John (compiler) (also known as the Astley collection). *A New General Collection of Voyages and Travels: Consisting of the Most Esteemed Relations, Which Have Been Hitherto Published in Any Language; Comprehending Everything Remarkable in Its Kind, in Europe, Asia, Africa and America*. Thomas Astley, Publishing Director. London. 1745–47 (online version).

Haley, Alex. *Roots*. Vintage Books. 1991. (First published in Great Britain by Hutchinson, 1977.)

Johnson, John William; Hale, Thomas A. and Belcher, Stephen (editors). *Oral Epics from Africa – Vibrant Voices from a Vast Continent*. Indiana University Press. 1997.

Inglis, Lucy. *Georgian London. Into the Streets*. Penguin Books. 2014.

Johnston, James H. *From Slave Ship to Harvard: Yarrow Mamout and the History of an African American Family*. Fordham University Press. 2012.

Kamran, Muska. *A Negro who could read and write the Arabic Language – African Muslim Slaves as Intermediaries in North American Plantations and African Colonies*. A thesis submitted to John Hopkins University in conformity with the requirements for the degree of Master of Arts. Baltimore, Maryland. April 2015.

Klein, Martin A. *Slavery and Colonial Rule in French West Africa*. Cambridge University Press. 1998.

Kolchin, Peter. *American Slavery: 1619–1877*. Harper Collins Canada Ltd. 1993.

Machat, J. *Documents sur les Établissements Français de l'Afrique Occidentale au XVIIIe siècle*. Paris. 1906.

Magee, Joan. *Loyalist Mosaic. A Multi-ethnic Heritage*. Dundurn Press, Toronto and Charlottetown. 1984.

Mame Kouna Sene. *The Legend of Samba Gueladio Diegui*. Etheopique Revue Negro-Africaine de Litterature et de Philosphie. January 1975.

Marschner, Joanna. *Queen Caroline – Cultural Politics at the Early Eighteenth-Century Court*. Yale University Press. 2014.

Meyler, David and Peter. *A Stolen Life: Searching for Richard Pierpoint*. Natural Heritage Books, Toronto. 1999.

Middleton, Arthur Pierce. *Tobacco Coast. A Maritime History of Chesapeake Bay in the Colonial Era*. The Mariners' Museum, Newport News, Virginia. 1953.

Middleton, Arthur Pierce. The Strange Story of Job Ben Solomon. *The William and Mary Quarterly*, Vol. 5 No. 3. Omohundro Institute of Early American History and Culture. Williamsburg, VA. July 1948.

Moore, Francis. *Travels into the Inland Parts of Africa, containing a description of Several Nations for the Space of Six Hundred Miles up the River Gambia*. London. 1723.

Moore, William. *The Gentlemen's Society at Spalding: Its Origin and Progress*. London. 1851.

Munir, Hassam. Allah. Muhammad. *Ayuba Diallo's Long Journey Back to Africa*. www.ihistory.co website. 2016.

Murray, Amanda. *All the Kings' Horses – A Celebration of Royal Horses from 1066 to the Present Day*. Robson Books, London. 2006.

Newby, Eric. *William Hoare of Bath*. Sutton Publishing, Stroud, Glos. April 1991.

Olusoga, David. Black and British. *A Forgotten History*. Macmillan, London. 2016.

Oxford Archaeology. *Cedars Park, Cheshunt. Archaeological Investigations and Recordings of Structural Remains*. April 2008.

Park, Mungo. *Travels in the Interior of Africa – Volume 01*. Cassell & Company. 1893.

Postlethwayt, Malachy. *The Universal Dictionary of Trade and Commerce, with Large Additions and Improvements, Adapting the Same to the Present State of British Affairs in America Since the Last Treaty of Peace Made in the Year 1763*. London. 1774.

Postlethwayt, Malachy. *The importance of the African expedition considered*. C. Say, Newgate Street, London. 1758.

Rediker, Marcus. *The Slave Ship – A Human History*. John Murray, London. 2007.

Reeve, Henry Fenwick. *Gambia: Its History Ancient, Medieval And Modern together with Geographical Geological And Ethnological Conditions and a description of The Birds, Beasts And Fishes Found Therein.* John Murray, London. 1912.

Rennell, Major James and others. *Proceedings of the Association for Promoting the Discovery of the Interior Parts of Africa*, Vol. 1 (including Mungo Park's expedition from the River Gambia), London. 1810.

Robinson, David; Curtin, Philip and Johnson, James. *A tentative Chronology of Futa Toro from the Sixteenth through the Nineteen Centuries.* Cahiers D'Etudes Africaines. Vol. 12, No. 48. 1972

Sarr, Assan. *Islam, Power, and Dependency in the Gambia River Basin – The Politics of Land Control, 1790–1940.* University of Rochester Press, USA. 2016.

Scheub, Harold. *African Tales.* The University of Winconsin Press, USA. 2005.

Thomas, Hugh. *The Slave Trade – The History of the Atlantic Slave Trade: 1440–1870.* Simon & Schuster, New York. 1997.

Van der Kiste, John. *King George II and Queen Caroline.* Sutton Publishing, Stroud, Glos. 1997.

Walls, Bruce. *Tales of old Dover.* Spectator Books. 1977.

Walvin, James. *The Slave Trade.* Thames & Hudson, New York. 2011.

White, Jerry. *London in the Eighteen Century. A Great and Monstrous Thing.* The Bodley Head. 2012.

Wikle, Thomas A. and Lightfoot, Dale R. Landscapes of the Slave Trade in Senegal and The Gambia. *Focus on Geography,* Vol. 57, No. 1. Spring 2014.

Index

◇◇◇